HUTCHINSON SCIENCE LIBRARY

★

ANIMAL POPULATIONS

T. O. BROWNING, B.Sc., Ph.D.

ANIMAL POPULATIONS

Science Today Series

HARPER & ROW, PUBLISHERS

NEW YORK AND EVANSTON

HARPER & ROW, PUBLISHERS, *Incorporated*
49 East 33rd Street, New York 16, U.S.A.

Printed in Great Britain

FOR ANN KNOWS WHO,
AND DEN KNOWS WHY

Contents

'. . . it is plain that the more you recede from your grounds, the weaker do you conclude; and as in nature, the more you remove yourself from particulars, the greater peril of error do you incur . . .'

BACON: "*The advancement of learning*".

Preface

This book is an attempt to present, in a simple way, the study of natural populations of animals as a quantitative and experimental branch of science. Too often ecology is regarded by laymen and ecologists alike as being the mere description, detailed and precise though it may be, of areas of landscape and the animals and plants found to be living in them, with perhaps some suggestions about the ways in which the various species influence one another. But this is natural history and not science. It is 'stamp collecting', not 'physics'. If ecology is to be scientific, the necessary natural history must give rise to hypotheses, and the hypotheses must be testable experimentally and lead to general conclusions, even though the conclusions will usually be limited in scope. Only then does ecology rightfully take its place alongside physiology as a branch of biological science.

The scope of this book is limited to the study of populations; the ecology of communities is not touched upon. The book takes a partisan stand on the way in which the changes one observes in the numbers of animals in a natural population are best to be explained. I have set out the main ideas that have been developed recently by Andrewartha, Birch and myself (see Andrewartha and Birch, 1954; Andrewartha and Browning, 1961; Browning, 1962) and have deliberately not included any discussion of other points of view for the sake of brevity and simplicity. A short list of important works setting out alternative points of view is included with the references.

Although this is a small book, and an elementary one, I have included references to original papers which also serve as an index of authors, because I have found that a book without references is like an egg without salt; it may be nutritious but it leaves no after-taste. In some cases, particularly in the long series

9

by A. Milne on *Ixodes ricinus*, where I have drawn heavily on a number of papers, only one reference is given. This is to the most recent paper, and includes references to earlier work.

I have assumed that the reader comes to this book with no previous knowledge of animal ecology but a fair grounding in biology, physics and chemistry. Chapter 1 is an account of the ecology of the sheep-tick *Ixodes ricinus* in Great Britain. I have put it first and set it out in some detail for a number of reasons. It illustrates the way in which a complex problem in population ecology can be unravelled, and introduces many of the ideas that are discussed later in the book. I use it as a foundation on which to build the abstract ideas of a population and an environment. It is more usual to state general propositions first and then to illustrate them with examples, but I have found that students coming to ecology for the first time do not, as a rule, have sufficient facts at their command to enable them to grasp easily the generalisations with which they have to deal. In Chapters 2 and 3 the ideas of a population and an environment are developed and the concept of probability is introduced as central to the understanding of the ecology of populations. In Chapters 4 to 8 I give additional examples of the ways in which the environment of an animal may influence the numbers in a population, and Chapters 9 and 10 are concerned with some of the complexities that can arise, and how they fall into the general scheme. Chapter 11 is an attempt to show man's place in the ecology of other animals and to suggest the most important aspects of the ecology of man.

My colleague, Dr. H. G. Andrewartha has been very long-suffering with me in my attempts to bend his ideas into a more satisfactory shape, and I should like to thank him for it. Prof. LaMont C. Cole and Dr. J. N. Black were kind enough to read the manuscript, and their criticisms were most helpful. My wife has had to sit and listen to long passages, and she knows how much the writing gained in clarity from her criticism. I must also thank Mrs. P. E. Madge for the pains she took in preparing the figures, and Mrs. R. Twist and Miss Barbara Stead for their untiring work preparing and checking the typescript.

1

A Study in the Highlands

1.1
INTRODUCTION

In the high, rough moors of the north of England, Scotland and Wales lives the sheep-tick, *Ixodes ricinus*. *Ixodes* is important to farmers because it sucks the blood of sheep and thereby spreads the disease known as 'louping-ill'. The tick, when it first hatches from the egg, is a six-legged *larva*. It crawls to the top of a grass-stem, where it waits for a while. If a sheep, or any other warm-blooded animal, brushes it in passing, the larva will leave the grass-stem and cling to the sheep until it has engorged itself with blood. Then it falls to the ground and, having digested its meal, moults its 'skin' to emerge into the next stage of the life-cycle as an eight-legged *nymph*. A year later the nymph seeks a meal in the same way as the larva did. The nymph, when fully fed, also drops to the ground and moults to become an *adult*. The adult males do not require food, but the females do; nevertheless, both sexes climb grass-stems to seek hosts. The females feed, but the males wander about apparently aimlessly on the host until they find a female. Whether or not they find a female, they drop off exhausted after a few days and die. When the females have finished feeding they also drop off the host and, if they have mated, produce a batch of about 2000 eggs; then they, too, die. The whole process from egg to adult occupies about three years, because each stage is active, that is, in a position to attach itself to a host and feed, only in the spring, so there is time for only one feed and one moult each year. The rest of the year is spent on the ground.

Feeding in *Ixodes* is a long-drawn-out and complex affair. The time required to feed and the amount of blood ingested depends on the stage of the life-cycle, as shown in Table 1. In all stages the

amount of blood taken is much greater than the original weight
of the unfed tick – the tick virtually engorges itself with blood.

Table 1

Feeding time and amount of blood taken by three stages of
Ixodes ricinus

Stage	Days for feeding	Weight before feeding (in mg.)	Weight after feeding (in mg.)
Larva	3–4		
Nymph	4–5		4
Adult female	7–12	1·8	270
Adult male	—	1·2	—

Ticks have been found to attack a very wide range of hosts, so
wide, in fact, that it seems they will feed on any mammal or bird
which comes in contact with them during the period when they
are active. But in Britain the host that men are concerned about,
and the commonest mammal on the high grazing land, is the
sheep, and it is because *Ixodes* carries louping-ill and is therefore
an important economic problem that the beautiful story of its
ecology was worked out, mainly by Alec Milne, and can be told
here (see Milne, 1950, and earlier papers).

1.2

THE PROBLEM

When Milne began work on the ecology of *Ixodes*, the farmers
already knew that louping-ill was confined to the high moorland
grazings and was absent from lowland pastures, notwithstanding
the fact that the lowland grazings are lusher and carry more
sheep per acre. And they knew that the disease was transmitted
by the tick; but no-one knew whether ticks could become
established in lowland pastures and so spread the disease to these
areas.

There was also a puzzling state of affairs in the highlands,
where certain farms, or fields, were known to be free from ticks,
while neighbouring farms or fields had been infested for years.
And certain fields which had never carried ticks became infested
and, once infested, remained so. It was important, then, to know
where ticks were already established, where they could live, and
the reasons why ticks live in some places and not in others.

Farmers were well aware that their sheep became infested with ticks in the springtime, while at other times of the year few or no ticks could be found on them. Here again were questions that required to be answered. What are the reasons why ticks become abundant on sheep in spring, and why are they not to be found at other times, and how do they survive the intervening period? Does a tick that does not get a meal one year survive to get another chance the next year?

Finally, in areas that were known to harbour ticks, there were places where ticks seemed to be more numerous than in others. And it was possible that in some years ticks were more numerous than in other years. Again a series of questions arose. Do the numbers of ticks in an area change and, if so, how much do they change, and what are the reasons for the change? All these questions relate to the *distribution and numbers* of ticks – they are questions that ecology deals with. It is because the answers to most of these were worked out with such precision that I am going to use the ecology of *Ixodes* as the model to illustrate what I think are the important principles of animal ecology.

1.3

THE AREA

Most of Milne's work was done in northern England, in Northumberland and Cumberland, but other earlier workers, notably McLeod and Moore, has studied the tick in Scotland and Wales as well, and Milne was able to make use of their findings.

Farms on the moors are large by English standards, between 1000 and 4000 acres, but they carry sheep, usually the long-woolled Swaledale, Blackface or Cheviot breeds, at the rate of no more than one sheep per acre. The vegetation consists of rough bent grasses, mostly *Nardus stricta*, bracken or heather, with trees or shrubs only on the banks of streams, or in small areas of 'scrub', or in plantations. A few fields are developed to finer grasses but even these often have incursions of bracken growing in them. Milne says: 'The common impression of hill and moor-land grazing country is of a treeless "waste" of rough grass, heather and bracken. Indeed, about 97% of a typical hill farm is grass or heather with bracken. But we would draw attention to the invariable 2–3% made up of small plantations, small scrub areas, small aggregates of trees or bushes, or individual trees and bushes, scattered within a typical grazing.' He found that these areas harboured a large number of small birds and mammals, which without them would not have been able to live in the hills, and which were of some importance to *Ixodes*, as will be seen later.

The soil of hill farms is usually damp clay-loam near the base of the hills and in the valleys, and sandy and well drained on the higher slopes. It is usually covered with a mat of dead and slowly decaying vegetation which varies considerably in depth, sometimes being as much as 6 inches. On one farm, for example, variation from 0·5 to 2·5 inches was found in different parts of the same pasture. On lowland pastures this mat is virtually non-existent.

The whole of the north of England is cool and moist. The rainfall is high, but the highlands receive more rain than the lowlands. Temperatures are moderate, rarely rising above 80°F in summer, and the weekly average maximum temperature is around 50°F even in winter. The humidity is high for most of the year, the average maximum being always well over 90% RH[1] and the average minimum varying from about 60% RH in the drier areas to about 70% RH in the more humid places.

1.4

THE TICKS

A good deal was known about *Ixodes* before Milne started his work, and much more information was added largely through the studies of A. D. Lees, who worked in collaboration with Milne (Lees, 1946, 1948; Lees and Milne, 1951).

It was found that ticks cannot survive long periods of drought, in fact, whenever the moisture in the air falls below about 92% RH ticks lose water by evaporation. For example, adult ticks survived less than one day at 0% RH and 2–3 days at 30% RH, but lived for three months or more when the humidity was over 90% RH. Nymphs and larvæ are even less tolerant of dryness. But Lees showed that at higher humidities ticks which had not

1. RH stands for relative humidity wherever it is used in this book.

recently fed were able to absorb water from the air. In this way they can tolerate short periods of drought, provided these are followed by periods when the humidity rises above about 92% RH. Engorged nymphal ticks are unable to absorb water from humid air, and lose water even more rapidly than unfed ticks, but if they survive until they moult they again become capable of replacing small amounts of water from very humid air.

Lees studied the behaviour of ticks in the laboratory. He found that in very humid air unfed ticks soon came to rest and would lie quiescent almost indefinitely, whereas in dry air they were restless and walked about most of the time. Given a choice of dry or moist air, ticks, whether engorged or unfed, came to rest in moist air after quite a short time.

Ticks that were collected from the field in the spring were presented in the laboratory with glass rods. They immediately climbed to the top and then turned round and began to descend. After quite a short time they turned upwards again. This behaviour was repeated many times. But if the humidity at the top of the rod was much lower than near the bottom, the distance the ticks descended was much shorter; they avoided the moist air and so were confined near the top of the rod, just as in the field they remain at the tip of a grass-stem where they may be picked up by a passing sheep. But in Lees' experiments the ticks did not stay for long at the tops of the rods. In the dry air they lost water, and after a period no longer avoided the humid air but descended to the bottom where the air was more moist.

These experiments made it clear that ticks were likely to survive only in places where the humidity was high, and showed that if an engorged tick once found a suitably humid spot it was unlikely to move from it until it was ready to seek another meal. On the other hand, during the period when the ticks were seeking a meal, a low humidity near the soil would keep them on the stems and fronds where they were likely to meet a host. Finally, these experiments showed that ticks did not remain long at the grass-tips, being forced to descend as they lost water.

Lees was able to observe the reactions of ticks to various stimuli while they were resting near the top of a glass rod. When they reached their final position near the top the ticks would fold their legs in a characteristic fashion, but as soon as they were aroused they would raise their forelegs in a 'questing' attitude and often move around the rod. The ticks behaved in this way if the rod moved, if a shadow fell on them, or if they experienced a light gust of warm air. These are the kinds of stimuli that, in nature, the ticks might receive from a sheep passing close to them. The ticks in the experiments would grasp at almost any object that passed near them. They soon dropped off 'neutral' objects such as cotton-wool, but clung tenaciously to warm-bodied animals. It is easy to see how these experiments throw light on the ability of ticks to find and cling to a host.

Hungry ticks were attracted to objects, such as test-tubes provided these were warmer than the ambient air, and the attraction was greatly increased if some 'attractive' substance like fleece-wool was also present. The hair from a variety of animals was shown to be attractive provided it was warm – about 37°C.

Ticks were always found to move away from an intensely directed source of light, but unfed ticks would move upwards on a rod towards moderate illumination. Recently engorged ticks, on the other hand, always moved away from the source of light and would keep moving until they found some place at least slightly shaded.

We shall see presently how these studies in physiology and behaviour greatly helped Milne to interpret correctly his ecological observations of ticks in the field, and also suggested relevant experiments to be carried out in the field.

1.5

ECOLOGY

1.51 *Seasonal activity*

The first thing that had to be done in elucidating the ecology of *Ixodes* was to make precise observations on the numbers of ticks found on sheep at different times throughout the year. In this way, the periods when ticks were actively seeking food, and when they were relatively quiescent, could be determined. Ten one-year-old sheep were used on each farm studied and the numbers of adult ticks on them were counted each week. Larvæ and nymphs are small and extremely difficult to count on the sheep, but it was found that nymphs and larvæ would cling to a blanket dragged over the ground – they could then be easily counted. The blanket was 2 yards wide and was always dragged for 50 yards over the pasture, giving a standard measure of the number of ticks active on 100 square yards of pasture.

The numbers of ticks recorded in the curves of Figure 1 represent samples taken in 1940 of the ticks on the vegetation on two farms, Crag and Hethpool, ready to cling to the sheep or the

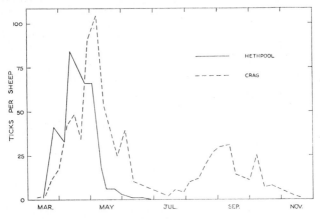

Figure 1

Changes observed throughout the year in the numbers of ticks found on sheep on two farms in northern England. After Milne.

blanket. They represent the numbers of ticks that were 'active', that is, ready to seize a host, at the time the samples were taken and do not represent the actual numbers of ticks present on the grazings. The difference in activity in autumn on the two farms remains a puzzle.

The curves in Figure 1, rising rapidly from near zero in winter, show that ticks, lying quiescent in the mat of vegetation during winter, become active in spring, emerging from the mat over a period of several weeks. But why does the curve fall away as it does as summer approaches? Is it because all the ticks are gradually picked up by the sheep and, having fed, are no longer available to be picked up again, or do those that do not find a host fairly quickly die, and so reduce the numbers available to be picked up?

The experiment that threw light on these questions was done by selecting a number of sites on a farm and placing at each site about twenty-four individually marked adult male and female ticks. The sites were covered with an open-mesh cage to keep stock and predators out and were watched almost daily, records being kept of the times when each tick was seen crawling at the tips of the vegetation inside the cages. The results of this work are illustrated in Figure 2 and show a striking resemblance to the activity curves in Figure 1. But because it was possible to recognise individual ticks, much more information could be gathered. The detailed behaviour of a number of these ticks is illustrated in Figure 3, which shows that there was a great deal of variability between individual ticks.

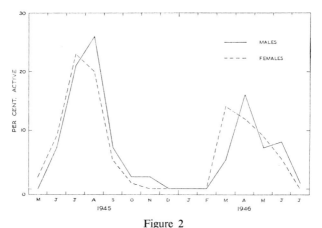

Figure 2

Proportion of marked adult ticks seen crawling on vegetation at intervals throughout two years. After Milne.

In general, however, a tick would be active, that is, sitting at the tips of a stem, for only two or three days at a time. Then it would disappear into the mat and remain hidden in the dense vegetation for a week or more. After this it would reappear, usually on the same stem as before. The whole period during which a tick was thus intermittently active was, on the average, only five weeks, and in this time it emerged from the mat and

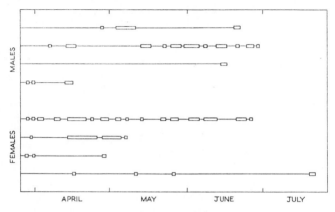

Figure 3

The periods of activity of a few individual ticks. The lines represent periods when the individual was not visible, and hence presumably inactive in the mat. The rectangles represent periods when the individual was visible on the vegetation. After Milne.

climbed to the tips three or four times. Individuals differed considerably from one another in the duration of their active lives: the time spent at the tips in any one sortie, the time spent in the mat between sorties and the number of times they climbed the stems. It soon became clear that, although the period of activity of the population of 48 ticks occupied some seven months, individual ticks were active for only a small proportion of that time; on a pasture, then, at any one moment during the period when the ticks are active and sheep are being infested, only a small proportion of the ticks will be in a position to be picked up by the sheep. This study also showed that a tick that had been active in spring but that did not find a meal disappeared into the mat and was never seen again. Thus ticks do not survive from one year to the next unless they have fed.

1.52 *Dispersal and survival of ticks on the ground*

It was well known that when the sheep-tick has finished feeding it drops from its host and falls to the ground, wherever the host may be. And there was good evidence that its chance of survival is small if it falls on ground that is not covered with a dense mat. It became important, then, to know something about the ability of engorged ticks to move about in search of a suitable place to live in. So groups of 20 male ticks and 20 females which had just finished feeding were placed on the ground in a variety of situations on hill pastures. After an interval, a square of turf with a side eight inches long was cut from the ground around the spot at which ticks were laid down. Then a strip of turf four inches wide surrounding the square was removed, and the ticks in both the square and the strip were counted. Out of a total of 400 ticks placed on the ground, 220 were recovered from the central square and eight from the surrounding strip of turf. The rest were not seen again. Other observations confirmed the conclusion that ticks, once they reach the ground, do not move more than a very few inches horizontally from the place where they fall.

In an experiment in which eight engorged females were placed on short fescue grass three inches away from a dense clump of bent, only three found their way into the bent, and the paths followed by the ticks led Milne to describe them as having 'blundered' into the clump by chance. Four of the ticks were eaten by predators within a very short time, their swollen bodies being obvious in the short grass. The eighth wandered about and eventually stopped near the bent, but not in it. In another experiment on a short fescue sward, six engorged female ticks were dropped during summer and their movements followed. All but one were seen to move only a few inches and finally died of desiccation, their bodies shrivelled and blackened. None of these succeeded in hiding itself and none moved more than three inches from the point at which it was dropped.

These experiments, together with the information on the rate at which ticks lose water when the air around them is dry, made it clear why ticks are not found on lowland pastures. On a fine grass sward there are few places where the humidity will remain high enough during summer to prevent the tick losing water, and unless a tick happens to fall on or very near such a place it has no way of finding it. So although ticks may be brought to lowland pastures, they very soon die out. It remained to explain how ticks manage to persist on highland grazings.

Careful measurements of humidity in the mat of decaying vegetation showed that where the mat was thick, say, three inches or more, the air deep in the mat was always saturated with water vapour, or nearly so. This was true even at the height of summer. Even in the topmost half-inch of the mat the humidity was found to be much higher, on the average, than in the air above the mat. Humidity in the top half-inch was measured on 88 occasions in spring and summer, and on only 20 of these was the reading below 98% RH, the average being 92% RH. At the same time the average for the air near the tips of the vegetation was 70% RH. Thus, since ticks of all stages lose water rapidly below 90% RH, a tick in the mat would be much less exposed to desiccation than one that was not so protected, and its chance of surviving the summer could be expected to be much greater. The next step, then, was to find out where ticks actually live: on top of the mat or within it.

Even on heavily infested pastures there is probably not more than one adult female tick to each four square yards, so searching for ticks in the mat would be a time-consuming and not very rewarding business. But since a tick does not move horizontally more than a couple of inches from the spot where it falls to the ground, it was practicable to drop ticks on a marked spot and find them again at a later date. The procedure, then, was to drop 20 male and 20 female ticks, unfed, over a small area, and later to return and dig up the turf, complete with an inch of underlying soil. Then vegetation stems were shaved off the layer and the soil was removed, leaving the mat. In some cases it was possible to distinguish between an open-textured upper mat and a more compacted, peaty, lower mat, and in these cases the mat was sliced at the junction between the two. The sections of turf were then broken up carefully and searched for ticks. The results were clear-cut: 20 out of a total of 699 ticks recovered were found in the standing vegetation, and all these were 'active', since they clung to Milne's hands while he was cutting the turf. Five were recovered from the soil, and 674 were found in the mat. In those cases where it was possible to subdivide the mat, 493 ticks were found in the upper mat and 71 in the lower. Thus 99% of inactive ticks were found in the mat, and of these 87% were in the upper part.

Although this showed that unfed ticks lived in the mat, it was also necessary to find out whether the engorged female could, in fact, penetrate among the thatch of stems and fronds. The

engorged female is so large and so sluggish that it can easily be
followed in the field. Milne described what happens when an
engorged female is dropped on the ground. It is at first supported,
as a rule, 'on the criss-cross of growing grass-stems and rushes
fairly high up in the vegetation layer. It immediately begins to
seek a way downwards, clumsily and slowly. Its efforts appear
grotesquely feeble because of the enormous disproportion of legs
to swollen body; yet the tick manages to bore down through the
dense labyrinth of vegetation, dragging itself out of sight.' The
tick continues to struggle downwards for about a week, and in
this time progresses between one quarter of an inch and one and
one-half inches. It is able to move sideways only during the period
it spends before entering the mat and, as we saw, the distance it
travels is usually no more than two or three inches.

The engorged female tick, then, having dropped to the ground,
never again emerges. If it falls in a suitable place where it can
burrow into the mat it may survive for about two months and lay
a batch of some 2000 eggs. Soon after this it dies. The larvæ that
hatch from the eggs will, because of their mother's industry, find
themselves in a situation where there is enough moisture to give
them a high probability of surviving until it is time to climb the
stems in search of a meal. If the spot on which the female falls is
unsuitable, she is likely to die of desiccation long before she can
lay any eggs. Nymphs and larvæ also fall from the host and their
chance of survival until the next spring similarly depends on
whether or not they can find adequate shelter in the place where
they land. The moist mat ensures that the ticks do not become
dried out during summer, and this is one of the major problems
facing the engorged tick. But in his observations of individual
ticks, Milne frequently found that a tick would disappear or
would be torn open as if some other animal had attacked it.

1.53 *Predators*

A number of species of animal living in the moorland grazings
seemed to qualify as predators of ticks. Many of these were
collected and kept in small cages or jars with engorged ticks.
Spiders, centipedes, ground beetles and other insects ignored the
ticks completely. But when ticks were confined on the ground in
the wide, wire-mesh cages (to exclude birds), some were found,

nevertheless, to have been killed. It seemed, then, that lizards or small rodents were the likely culprits. Using traps made of tins sunk in the ground, and placing live engorged ticks in them, Milne showed that only when shrews (*Sorex araneus*) fell into the traps were the ticks eaten. The ticks either disappeared, or the remaining piece was part of the empty 'shell' rent open in a characteristic and recognisable fashion. This did not occur when voles – the only other small rodent of the moors – were in the trap; they ignored the ticks.

Birds also eat ticks. This was neatly demonstrated by exposing engorged ticks in two places, in one of which a wire-mesh cage kept birds away, whilst the other was open to all comers. Table 2 shows that the proportion missing, and therefore probably eaten by predators, was much greater where birds had access to the ticks. And birds leave no remains.

Table 2

Fate of engorged female ticks in the presence of predators

	Birds excluded	Birds not excluded
Killed by shrews	46	50
Missing	9	44
Survived	36	6
Died from other causes	9	0

This table shows the extremely hazardous life an engorged tick must lead until it is well buried in the mat. And this after it has succeeded in obtaining a meal, which is itself a very chancy business.

1.54 *Finding a meal*

Milne made an extensive study of the animals on which ticks were found and concluded that any mammal or bird that was likely to come in contact with the grass, bracken or heather of tick-infested land was a potential host for ticks. However, if we put ourselves in the place of a tick for a moment (a salutary exercise for an ecologist) it is clear that our chance of getting a meal depends greatly on how many potential hosts are in our vicinity, and which species are present. A large, slow-moving, grazing animal would provide a better chance of a meal than a small insect-eating bird. So Milne set himself the task of estimating the proportion of the tick population on typical hill grazings that fed on each species of bird and mammal that lived in those areas. To do this he needed to know the average numbers of ticks of each stage found on each species of host, and the number of individuals of each species of host over each of the areas he was studying. He trapped and shot samples of each species, counted all the ticks he found on them and noted which stage in its life-cycle each tick had reached.

The first observation that emerged from the studies was that only a little over half the species of mammals living on a farm ever serve as hosts to adult female ticks (the males, although they cling to hosts, seldom feed). These were the larger animals, including domestic stock, man and wild animals such as roe deer, badgers, hares, rabbits and hedgehogs. Female ticks were never found on the smaller vole, shrew or field-mouse. And only three large birds, pheasant, grouse and magpie, out of the thirty-nine species known to be hosts to other stages, were found to carry the large female ticks. When the immature stages, nymphs and larvæ, were considered, the situation was quite different; all potential hosts, with the possible exception of the tiny shrew, were found to carry nymphs, and all carried larvæ.

The next point to emerge was the great differences found in the average numbers of ticks carried by different species of hosts. The sheep was by far the most heavily infested animal found on the hills. Milne used the sheep as his standard and set out to estimate the numbers of ticks carried by different species of hosts relative to the number carried by an average sheep ' going on the same ground' at the same time. For example, he would shoot a roe deer, count all the ticks on it, and then take a random sample of eight to ten sheep from the same field and count the ticks on them. Or he would shoot four grouse on one day and one on another, count all the ticks on each grouse, and compare these counts with the number of ticks found on a sample of sheep taken on each of the days of shooting from the same fields in which the grouse were shot. This method may seem laborious, but, because of the variability between the numbers of ticks on different fields, and the variability between the numbers of ticks active on different days, it was the only method that would give reliable results. In this way the wild hosts could be arranged in order of the average number of female ticks they carried relative to the numbers carried by sheep.

Table 3

Contribution of various species to food for tick population

Species	Relative no. of ticks per animal	Average no. of animals per farm	Relative no. of ticks fed (average)
Sheep	1·000	590	590·00
Roe deer	0·140	3	0·42
Hedgehog	0·135	12	1·62
Brown hare	0·077	20	1·54
Stoat	0·055	16	0·87
Badger	0·054	2	0·11
Otter	0·032	2	0·06
Fox	0·023	4	0·09
Pheasant	0·020	42	0·85
Red grouse	0·002	322	0·55
Magpie	0·002	3	0·01
Rabbit	0·001	692	0·97
Total			597·09

Mean percentage of female ticks fed by wild fauna   1·2
Range over five farms   0·8 – 1·4

The second column of Table 3 shows that, on the average, if a hundred ticks were found on a sheep, we could expect about fourteen on a roe deer, about two on a fox and only about one on ten rabbits. But in order to estimate the importance of the wild fauna as a whole in providing food for ticks it was necessary to know the average numbers of each species that lived on a hill farm. Milne was able, with the aid of gamekeepers' records, shepherds' and trappers' observations, published records, and his own observations, to arrive at an estimate of the numbers of each species of host that lived on each of five farms. These figures are shown in column three of Table 3. Then, by multiplying the relative number of ticks per animal by the number of individuals for each species, he arrived at an estimate of the relative numbers of female ticks that were fed by each species of host. These figures are given in the last column of Table 3, and it can be seen that out of every 597 female ticks that find a meal, 590 feed on sheep's blood. The striking fact in all this work was that although the estimates were made separately for each of five farms the results agreed closely – the proportion of ticks feeding on the wild fauna varied only between 0.8% to 1.4% between the five farms.

One point that is brought out forcibly by Table 3 is that although, on the average, a roe deer feeds about one hundred times as many ticks as a rabbit, yet the deer population on the farms is less than half as important in providing food for ticks as is the rabbit population, simply because there are 200 times as many rabbits. Many such relationships can be seen in the table.

The number of wild animals and birds that serve as hosts to nymphs is considerably greater than those on which adults are found, so one would expect that the proportion of nymphs fed by the wild fauna would be greater than was the case with females. There is another reason why this should be so. Milne found that whereas sheep picked up, on the average, about seven nymphs for every female, rabbits picked up about eighty nymphs to each female, and large birds over forty to one. So for this reason, also, the wild animals on hill farms might be expected to provide food for a greater proportion of the nymphs than the females. Using a method similar to that described for females, Milne was, in fact, able to estimate that the wild fauna provided food for between 10% and 20% of the nymphs that obtained a meal.

It was impracticable to count larvæ on sheep and so an equivalent comparison for larvæ could not be made. But Milne did estimate the numbers of nymphs relative to larvæ found on rabbits, mice, large birds and small birds, and showed that the very small species of wild fauna, which contribute only negligibly to the food for nymphs and not at all to the food for adults, nevertheless fed large numbers of larvæ. For example, a rabbit may feed three or four larvæ for every nymph picked up – but a field mouse will provide food for fifty larvæ for every nymph. The same holds for small birds compared with large birds. And when it is remembered that there are hundreds and may be thousands of small rodents in each acre of moorland, their contribution to the food of larval ticks can be seen to be considerable. Nevertheless, Milne considered that they still did not contribute as much as the sheep flock. The large number of species of wild animals and birds on hill farms is perhaps surprising because of the apparent desolation of the country, and Milne attributed their being able to live in the hills 'to the invariable 2–3 % of the area covered by plantations, trees or bushes', as was mentioned in Section 1.3.

With all this background information to draw on, Milne was in a position to try to measure the numbers of ticks on different parts of the hills, with a good chance of being able to explain his results satisfactorily.

1.55 *The numbers of ticks on hill farms*

On hill farms the depth of the mat of decaying vegetation varies considerably from place to place. Table 4 shows the results of counts of ticks on blankets dragged over pastures with different thicknesses of underlying mat.

Table 4

Numbers of nymphs caught on different thicknesses of mat

Plot	1	2	3
Mean no. of nymphs per drag	0·2	2·2	5·1
Thickness of mat in inches	0·5 – 1·0	0·7 – 3·1	1·5 – 5·2

The results were clear: more ticks were found on pastures where the mat was deep than where it was thin.

But the number of ticks on a pasture can hardly be related only to the depth of the mat; the number of sheep in the area must also be important, since this will determine the chance of finding a meal and so of survival. Now hill sheep, having spent the hours of daylight grazing the lower slopes and valleys, move upwards at night and congregate on easily recognisable areas known as 'lairs'. The lairs occupy only a small proportion of the area of a farm and about half the sheep's time is spent on them, so that because many more ticks would drop off the sheep on the lairs than on any other area of comparable size, one might expect the numbers of ticks on the lairs to be high. Also, an active tick should have a much better chance of finding food on the lairs than elsewhere. But this idea is not supported by results. Two areas, one on a typical lair and one on the pasture, were sampled simultaneously on 66 occasions: 20 ticks were collected on the lair, and 355 on the pasture. The lower numbers on the lair were explained by examining the vegetation. It consisted of fine, short herbage on the dry ground of the hilltop, on which a tick would have little chance of survival. In this case the fact that there was an abundance of food on the lairs did not help at all, because the ticks that fell there would die long before they could feed.

A wide range of situations was studied with the blanket-dragging technique, and always the same result was found. Wherever the mat was thick and damp the number of ticks tended to be large, and *vice versa*. The explanation was that although at least comparable numbers of ticks would fall on both areas, their chances of finding adequate shelter from the dryness of summer were too small for their survival in any numbers.

Adequate shelter in summer, then, is one important condition for the survival of ticks, but where shelter is available we could predict, as we did above, that an adequate supply of hosts would be important to the ticks. Just how important was answered when Milne counted all the adult and nymphal ticks on an area of hill pasture. He laid out three parallel plots, each two by fifty yards, on a heavily infested field. A blanket was dragged twice over each plot almost every day during the whole of one season, that is, during the time when any ticks were active. By this method virtually the whole population on each plot was collected and counted and an estimate of the variability of the numbers of ticks on different plots could be made. The results are set out in Table 5.

Table 5

Ticks caught on three plots during one season of activity

Plot	No. of days' dragging	Males	Females	Nymphs
1	74	15	26	1009
2	74	11	9	700
3	74	7	22	715
Total	(148 *days per plot*)	33	57	2424

From these figures Milne computed that the total number of female ticks on the more heavily infested half of the field was between 70,000 and 116,000. (The two halves of the field differed and the plots had been laid out on the more heavily infested half.) At the same time as this work was being done, a flock of 150 sheep was running on the field, and by counting the number of ticks picked up each week by a group of 10 of these sheep, and knowing the length of time a female requires to become engorged, it was possible to estimate that the flock picked up between 15,000 and 45,000 female ticks during the season. These figures showed what no one had hitherto suspected, that a very high proportion of the ticks on the hills died of starvation, even when their principal host, the sheep, was maintained there at maximum numbers – about one sheep per acre. The same arguments applied to the other stages of the ticks, but the young stages were not studied in the same detail.

We saw earlier that summer drought seriously reduced the ticks' chances of survival, and that shrews and birds ate a high proportion of engorged ticks before they could get under cover in the mat. To these dangers must be added the rather low chance of obtaining a meal at each stage in the tick's life cycle. Milne estimated that 40% of the females probably find a host. If this proportion were the same for each of the immature stages, which would seem reasonable, it would mean that on the average, out of every hundred newly emerged larvæ, only seven would obtain the three meals necessary for them to have a chance of contributing progeny to the next generation. When the other dangers are added to the chance of starving, it can be seen that 2000 eggs per female is not really over-production.

The production of eggs by females, however, is entirely dependent on their having been fertilised by a male while they were feeding upon the host. This is the only place where the sexes can meet. It is important that male and female should be reasonably close together, for the male moves about quite at random and can perceive his mate from only a very short distance. In mid-spring, when most ticks are active, it is probable that both males and females are present on each sheep, but towards the end of the feeding season in early summer it must often happen that only one adult is present on a host at a time. In the case of the wild hosts the problem becomes very important, for in his counts Milne frequently found wild animals with only a single adult feeding on them. This adult was doomed to die without reproducing, even after having jumped all the other stiff hurdles set in its path during its previous three years of life.

These considerations went a long way to providing a rational explanation for the facts that were known about the way in which ticks occurred on farms. For example, it had long been thought that once a farm became infested with ticks it was only a matter of time before the ticks spread to neighbouring farms. It was known that a farm or a field could be infested by the introduction of a flock of sheep heavily infested with ticks, but it was widely held that, even when this did not occur, wild animals and birds would carry ticks from one farm to another through the fences and the infestation would spread. But Milne found a number of cases in which a farm, separated only by a wire fence from an infested farm, had remained free from ticks for many years, the wild animals, of course, moving freely from one farm to another. And he found no case in which a farm had become infested at a reasonably well-defined time where the explanation could not be that sheep had brought the ticks to the farm. The explanation of this was now clear. Of the few ticks brought to a grazing by wild animals, by far the majority of the survivors that found a host would be picked up by sheep. Since the numbers would be small and since they would become active at different times, the chance of their finding a mate on such a large animal would be negligible. In fact, one can visualise this as an added obstacle for the ticks on the infested land. They stand a chance, albeit a small one, of being picked up by a wild animal and carried into an area which is uninfested and so is just as lethal as being dropped on a sheep lair or a fine fescue sward. On the other hand, a whole flock of infested sheep bring to a new field such a large number of ticks that this new colony is likely to thrive and spread over the whole grazing.

Rational as this argument was, there seemed no way of testing it, except, perhaps, watching an uninfested field for ticks to appear on it. All the evidence pointed to an extremely slow build-up in the numbers of ticks once an infestation had started, and so this looked a most time-consuming and unlikely project, since there was no guarantee that a particular field chosen would ever become infested. But a lucky chance allowed a critical observation to clinch the idea. Milne had been studying three farms, Hethpool, Westnewton and Kilham, which lie in a straight line and show a gradient in the number of ticks on them. Hethpool was heavily infested, Westnewton less so, and on Kilham no tick had ever been seen, although the shepherd knew ticks and was on the look out for them. Studies of soil, vegetation and meteorology showed no similar trend which might explain the numbers of ticks. Then a boundary fence between one of the Kilham pastures and a fairly heavily infested pasture on a neighbouring farm fell into disrepair during the spring period of activity, and some infested sheep strayed for a while on to Kilham. In 1942 the first ticks were seen on Kilham, 'an odd tick on an odd sheep', as the shepherd said. By 1945 a sample of ten sheep running on Kilham at the height of the spring period of activity yielded a total of eight ticks – the comparable number on the heavily infested Hethpool at the same time was 214. This was evidence that sheep, even only a few, could start an infestation, provided they got into an uninfested pasture at a time when they were carrying large numbers of ticks.

Milne found evidence that the rate at which ticks increase in numbers on the hills is very low. This was shown by the observation that in one infested area, the College Valley in Northumberland, the original infestation occurred about 1870, the ticks being brought in on 'a flock of sheep bought at May Day from the notorious infested area of North Tyne . . . where ticks had always been'. Since then about 15 to 20 farms in the area had become infested. The original focus had been infested for about 80 years. Farms within a radius of 2–3 miles had been infested for between 30 and 60 years. Outside that area the infestation dated back 5 to 20 years, and some farms were still not infested. Milne found that those farms that had been recently infested had smaller numbers of ticks than those that were infested earlier. It seemed that 15 to 20 years were needed before the ticks attained their maximum numbers. There was no feature of the farms, other than their distance from the focus, that would account for the observed gradient in numbers.

1.6

CONCLUSION

This, then, is the story of the sheep-tick as Milne patiently and brilliantly unfolded it. It remains only to consider the gaps he left unfilled: things we do not know about ticks which we might expect could be found out, and which might increase our understanding of the ecology of *Ixodes*. First there is a little evidence that the number of ticks on a pasture fluctuates from year to year. This is quite apart from any steady increase following a new infestation. It implies that more ticks survive to become active in spring in some years than in others. The causes of this are unknown, and before we could hope to know them we should need to have accurate counts of ticks on a number of selected areas and over a number of years. Running concurrently with these counts we should need obervations and measurements on some of the things influencing the survival of ticks which would perhaps allow us to explain our observed fluctuations in numbers. This would not be impossible but would be very tedious, and the chances of arriving at an adequate explanation may not be very good in this particular case.

The other gap in our knowledge of ticks concerns the reasons for the burst of activity in spring. What is it that makes the tick become active in spring and cease activity in summer? And why are ticks active only in spring in some areas and in both spring and autumn in others? Milne searched in vain for an answer to these questions. That he did not find it and yet went on to explain most of the rest of the ecology of *Ixodes* argues that these causes may be very subtle and shows how, in science, it is sometimes wise to leave aside the incidental problem which is 'too hard' and get on with the main job, which is quite difficult enough as it is.

We shall now turn to the main purpose of this little book and see how the facts and ideas discussed in relation to *Ixodes* can be used to help build up a comprehensive theory which can serve as a basis for the study of the ecology of all animals.

2

The Idea of a Population

Ixodes ricinus is found in many parts of the British Isles and in Europe, northern Asia and northern Africa. Thus the species is split up by the sea into at least three large and geographically distinct groups. In ecology we find it useful to consider isolated groups of this kind separately, and we call them separate populations. It was originally thought that all sheep-ticks in Britain constituted a single population, but it was later shown that at least two distinct populations existed; those in the north-east of England, which became active only in spring, and those in Wales, the north-west of England and in Scotland, which became active in both spring and autumn. These two populations are distinguished not only geographically but also by their behaviour. It is possible that more extensive work on the western population would reveal a difference between, say, the ticks in Wales and those in Scotland, and we would then consider them also to be distinct populations. We cannot lay down any hard and fast rules for distinguishing populations of animals; the distinction between populations becomes apparent as our knowledge of a species increases.

Let us analyse the idea of a population a little further. We shall consider only the ticks in the north-east of England, as we did in Chapter 1. Milne set out to draw a map showing all the places in north-eastern England occupied by *Ixodes*. He did this by examining sheep on as many farms as possible and noting the farms on which he found ticks and those on which he consistently found none. Figure 4 shows the result. The shaded areas represent those places where ticks were found and the blank area where no ticks could be found. We say the shaded area represents the *distribution* of the population of *Ixodes*.

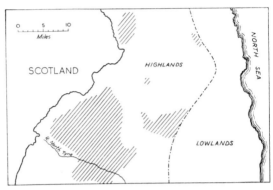

Figure 4

Map of north-eastern England showing the distribution of *Ixodes ricinus*. Ticks occur in the shaded areas only. After Milne.

Milne was also interested in the way in which the numbers of ticks varied from place to place within their area of distribution. Table 6 shows the number of female ticks found on ten sheep on three farms during the period when ticks were active. Because of the method used to take the samples, the numbers of ticks caught represent the relative number of ticks on each farm.

Table 6

Average number of female ticks per sheep on three farms

Hetha	Westnewton	Kilham
51·7	1·2	0

This is a measure of the *density* of ticks on the three farms. We can see that Kilham, with density zero, is outside the area of distribution of *Ixodes*. Thus the distribution and the density of a population are closely related: the distribution is that area within which the density is not zero.

Changes in the distribution of *Ixodes* can be brought about by infestation (as on Kilham – see section 1.55), sudden creation of favourable living conditions – often by bracken encroaching on a pasture of fine fescue grass and forming a mat – or the planting of fine sward on which ticks cannot survive in place of former mat-covered pasture.

Most of Chapter 1 was concerned with explaining the differences observed in the density of the tick population from place to place in the moorland farming country. But clearly, once we thoroughly understand the reasons for the changes in density of the population, we also understand how the tick comes to be distributed as it is, because we know why the density is zero in some places and not in others. The task of the ecologist, then, is to explain the density of the population he is studying, and this will entail an explanation of its distribution.

Not only can the density of a population be observed to vary from place to place, but also it can usually be shown to fluctuate with time. Fluctuations in the number of animals in a population require an explanation which it is the task of the ecologist to find, and we shall see later that the explanation often leads to a better understanding of changes in the distribution of a population.

If the number of animals in a chosen area is found to be increasing, then, whatever the actual causes may be, the observed increase can come about only for one of two reasons: either animals are moving into the area from outside, or the number of births in the population in a given time is greater than the number of deaths during the same period. If we neglect immigration for the time being, we see that whenever births in a population exceed deaths the density of the population increases, and conversely, whenever deaths exceed births the density declines. It is usual to express the number of births in a given period as a birth-rate, which is a measure of the *average* number of offspring produced by a female in a given time, and is obtained by dividing the total number of new individuals added to the population in some specified period by the number of females in the population at that time. For example, if we knew that 250 female ticks gave rise to 100,000 larvæ in a particular year, we should say that the birth-rate was 400 per female in that year. And since we know that females do not live more than one year our estimate of the birth-rate is 400 per female per generation.

The number of animals dying in a specified period can similarly be expressed as a death-rate. For example, if 100,000 larvæ hatched in early April, and within one week there were only 20,000 left alive, we should say that the death-rate among larvæ of that generation in the first week was either 800 per thousand or 0·8. If at the end of summer only 10,000 larvæ had obtained a meal and buried themselves in the mat, the death-rate would be 900 per thousand or 0·9 in that generation.

The speed at which the density of a population changes depends on the magnitude of the difference between the birth-rate and the death-rate in each generation. When the birth-rate greatly exceeds the death-rate, the numbers in each generation will increase rapidly; when the death-rate is slightly greater than the birth-rate, the numbers in each generation will decline slowly. It is usually more convenient to consider the rate of increase or decrease, not within a single generation, but over a relatively long period of time. In this case the rate at which the density changes depends not only on the average differences between birth- and death-rate in each generation but on the number of generations. This, in turn, will depend on the time required to complete a single generation, and so anything that influences the rate at which animals grow from birth to sexual maturity will influence the speed at which a population can increase or decrease in numbers. In *Ixodes* the duration of each generation is always three years, but in many animals the duration of a generation may vary considerably.

With most animals the individuals will be more variable with respect to the time taken to complete a generation, and we shall have to make use of the idea of the *average* duration of a generation. In practice this is estimated by observing a sample drawn at random from the population.

In estimating the birth-rate or the death-rate in a population we also have to observe a sample of individuals and estimate the performance of the average one. To revert to the examples I gave above: if, in certain circumstances, a sample of ticks lay, on the average, 400 eggs each; and if we know that under optimal conditions a tick may lay, on the average, 2000 eggs; then we may say that, in the circumstances, the chance that a tick will lay her full complement of eggs is 0·2. Or, if 100,000 larvæ, hatched in April, give rise to 10,000 nymphs next year, we may say that, in the circumstances, the chance of any one larva surviving to become a nymph is 0·1.

In other circumstances the ticks might lay more eggs, or more larvæ may survive, in which case the population may increase more rapidly. In general, any place where an individual's chance to survive and multiply is, on the average, great, is likely to have a dense population compared with a place where the individual's chance to survive and multiply is, on the average, small.

It is the ecologist's function to understand and explain the circumstances that influence an animal's chance to survive and multiply. This brings us to the idea of *environment*, which is discussed in Chapter 3.

3

The Idea of an Environment

In Chapter 1 we followed Milne in his efforts to explain the distribution and numbers of *Ixodes ricinus* in northern England. He found that ticks could become established only in places that afforded a sufficiently high chance that a female would obtain the three meals it needed, find a mate, and survive to lay eggs. Whether a particular place was suitable depended on many things.

A mat of decaying vegetation lying on top of the soil provided a moist situation all the year round, so that ticks were not exposed to drying winds and sun. Tall grass stems or bracken fronds provided a vantage-place from which a tick seeking a meal could easily grasp a host. But the likelihood of a host coming close enough for the tick to grasp it depended very much on the number of sheep and other warm-blooded animals that shared the pasture with the ticks, and also on their size, the larger animals affording a much greater chance of a meal than the smaller ones.

Despite the fact that they provided food for ticks, animals other than sheep constituted a definite threat, since they were not fenced in, and so ticks might drop off in a place quite unsuitable. They might fall in a field far away on ground not protected by a thick mat, or in a field in which no sheep grazed and so the chances of another meal would be small, or in a place where they were not amongst other ticks and so would have a small chance of finding a mate. Shrews and birds reduced the ticks' chance of survival by eating them before they could get deep into the protection of the mat. Man himself influenced the ticks' chance of survival and reproduction through his habits of building fences, maintaining a definite stocking-rate in his fields and preventing sheep from moving freely from one pasture to another, carrying ticks with them; also through his practice of moving sheep from one farm to another in large numbers, occasionally transporting a large number of ticks to new pastures that they would not otherwise reach.

All these things were shown to influence the ticks' chances of surviving and reproducing and thus, as was shown in Chapter 2, they influence the distribution and numbers of the population of *Ixodes*. It is convenient to have a collective name which will include all these things which influence an animal's chances of surviving and reproducing – we will call them the *environment* of an animal.

Every animal in a population can be thought of as having its own environment. In practice, however, we usually have to determine the average environment of the individuals in the population and to estimate the effect this has on the chances of survival and reproduction of the average individual.

It is worth noting here that there may be some things in the immediate vicinity of an animal that have no measurable influence on its chances of surviving and reproducing. Since, as scientists, we are concerned only with finding a system that will help us to explain our empirical observations about the distribution and numbers of animals, and not with providing a philosophical model, we consider these things *not* to be part of an animal's environment. Thus, starlight is not scientifically to be considered part of the environment of a tick. To this extent, then, the technical term 'environment' which I have introduced in this chapter differs from colloquial usage.

The list of things that we consider constitute the environment of a tick on a hill grazing is long, and, as it stands, unwieldy. In science, it is always convenient to classify the items making up any list under a few main headings, because in this way we will not only simplify an otherwise heterogeneous group, but also often discover relationships between items which were not immediately apparent. We can do this for the environment of a tick, and it turns out that the categories we choose can be applied quite generally to the environment of any animal.

First, then, there are in our list of things that influence a tick's chances of surviving and reproducing a number of things we normally think of as going to make up 'the weather.' Rain keeps the mat moist and so reduces the chance that a tick will become desiccated. The humidity of the air determines the rate at which the mat dries out, and also the length of time a tick can remain at the tips of stems waiting for a host. The velocity of the wind also influences the rate of evaporation of water from the mat, and if it is too strong the ticks are unable to climb the stems. Temperature influences the rate of evaporation and it also determines – to some extent at least – the periods when ticks can become active; at very low temperatures ticks remain completely inert. Thus these things influence ticks' chances of survival and reproduction in a number of different ways. However, because they are all intrinsically similar kinds of things, we are justified in lumping them all together in one category of the environment. We will call this category *weather*. It is important to notice that the term weather is used in a slightly different way here from its colloquial use. It refers to the weather experienced by the tick, in the place where it is living, and not to the weather that is measured in a Stevenson screen and reported in the daily press.

The tick, like any animal, is dependent for both survival and reproduction on an adequate supply of food, and we saw in section 1.54 that, in fact, less than half the female ticks on a pasture managed to obtain the food necessary before they could lay eggs; the rest starved to death. On a pasture on which the density of stocking was lower, a smaller proportion still of the females would have survived. And so we think of food as being abundant or scarce. It is also a commodity that is used by ticks. We also saw in section 1.5 that many ticks that do manage to secure a meal fall from their hosts to the ground and do not find adequate shelter before they are either eaten by predators or die from loss of water. They die because the shelter provided by the place where they fall is inadequate. In other places with a uniformly dense mat ticks will find shelter almost immediately. We can thus think of shelter also as being a commodity which ticks use and which may be abundant or in short supply. The two aspects of a tick's environment, food and shelter, are thus *resources* that the tick requires for survival and reproduction, and we can classify them together.

Warm-blooded animals are also part of the tick's environment, not only because they serve as food, but also because they are the only means whereby ticks can move any considerable distance, and because they serve as the meeting-places for the sexes. In both these roles they influence the tick's chances of survival and reproduction and are thus part of its environment. And because they are used by the tick we will classify them, along with food and shelter, as resources.

There is another part of the tick's environment that can usefully be thought of as a resource, and that is the stem up which it must climb in order to find a host.

It is essential for an adult tick to find a mate if it is to contribute progeny to the next generation, and so it is clear that *other ticks*, in so far as they are potential mates, are a component of a tick's environment. I shall call this category *members of the same species*. (This consideration reinforces the proposition put forward in Chapter 2, that the idea of an environment pertains to an individual and not to a population; otherwise we should have a population being part of its own environment, which is absurd.)

Warm-blooded animals are part of the environment of ticks because they provide food. But they also influence the tick's chance of survival in quite another way; shrews and birds prey on ticks quite heavily, and man moves sheep about and builds fences, in so doing influencing the tick's chances of survival and reproduction. We thus have another component of environment which I shall call *members of other species*.

Sometimes the influence of other species may be exerted in a roundabout way. For example, it would seem likely that foxes are a part of the environment of ticks in a way quite distinct from their occasionally providing food or some other resource. In Table 1 we saw that rabbits provided food for the greatest proportion of the tick population that fed on animals other than sheep. In the absence of foxes, rabbits might be more numerous on hill farms than they are, giving the ticks a slightly greater chance of obtaining a meal. In this way the fox would influence a tick's chances of survival and reproduction and so would be part of its environment. As a predator on the tick's food it would fall in the category 'members of other species'. In so far as it provides food for ticks it is part of the tick's resources. It is important to bear in mind that many parts of an animal's environment exert more than one distinct influence, and when they do they are part of two or more components of environment.

We have now pigeon-holed under four headings – *weather, resources, members of the same species,* and *members of other species* – almost all the things that were mentioned at the beginning of this chapter. There remains only one other category of factors that reduce a tick's chances of survival. Rocks on the hills provide rubbing-places where a sheep may scratch itself, and in doing so crush ticks feeding on it. Such objects we may call *hazards,* using the term as a concrete noun in the sense used in golf or steeple-chasing.

This analysis of the environment of the tick has now brought us to a point where we can place all the things that in any way influence a tick's chances of survival or reproduction into one of five categories – *weather, resources, members of the same species, members of other species* and *hazards.* In the next five chapters we shall explore these five components of environment further and try to show that they apply to a wide range of animals and that there are many and diverse ways in which they can exert their influence. In Chapter 9 we shall see how two or more of these components, acting together, influence one another and so modify their mutual effect on the animal.

4

Weather

In the next five chapters we shall consider the diversity of ways in which each of the components of environment may influence an animal's chance of surviving, the rate at which it grows to maturity, its chance of finding a mate, and the number of progeny it will leave behind it when it dies. We shall start by considering weather.

It will be convenient to think of weather as being the resultant of a number of separate components, such as temperature, moisture, wind, light and so on, and to study these one at a time, keeping everything else in the environment as constant as possible. In this way we can study, say, the influence of temperature on the rate of development of an animal or on some other aspect of its ecology, and when we have precise data on temperature under one set of environmental conditions, we can modify one of the other aspects of weather, say, moisture, and learn how this changes the effect of temperature on the animal. Finally, when our laboratory experiments are complete, we can go with more confidence into the field; we can observe the changes in the distribution and numbers of a natural population of the animals that we have studied and make measurements of the weather, and we should be in a good position to explain how the weather is contributing to the changes we observe.

Most of the examples in this chapter will be taken from laboratory studies, but it will be indicated how these have relevance to natural populations.

4.1

TEMPERATURE

The discussion in this section will be concerned with the influence of temperature on poikilothermic, or cold-blooded, animals, because with them the results are usually more striking than with homoiothermic, or warm-blooded, animals. The body temperature of poikilothermic animals is usually close to the temperature of their surroundings, but this is not always so. For example, the temperature of the thorax of the moth *Geotrupes* can rise 10°C above that of the surrounding air when the moth is vibrating its wings very rapidly preparatory to taking flight (Krogh and Zeuthen, 1941); and many insects have been shown to become much cooler than the air when water is evaporating rapidly from their bodies (Edney, 1957).

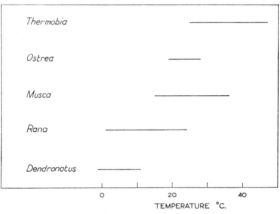

Figure 5

Range of temperature tolerable to five different animals. Note that there is no overlap between the temperatures tolerated by *Dendronotus* and either *Musca*, *Ostrea*, or *Thermobia*. After Andrewartha and Birch (1954).

When the temperature is extremely low, animals may die suddenly from freezing. At less extreme low temperatures they may die more slowly, without freezing. And at extremely high temperatures they may die more or less slowly from 'heat prostration', a complex physiological phenomenon. But between these two extremes there lies a zone of temperatures within which animals can live and flourish, and where we can detect no sign that the temperature itself is exerting any lethal influence on them. This zone of temperature has been called the 'tolerable range'. It varies widely from species to species, both in the range of temperature it includes and in the upper and lower limits. This is illustrated in Figure 5, where it can be seen that the tolerable range for *Dendronotus* lies between —1°C and 11°C, a range of 12°C, whereas for *Thermobia* the tolerable range covers 21°C, with the lower limit at 26°C and the upper limit at 47°C. We speak of the ranges of temperature above and below the limits of the tolerable range as being the zone of lethal high temperature and the zone of lethal low temperature.

4.11 *The influence of temperature on survival*

Animals that are kept indefinitely at temperatures outside their tolerable range will die after a longer or shorter time, depending upon the temperature, but provided the temperature is not too extreme most animals can survive short exposures that would be lethal if the exposure were prolonged. It is often desirable to estimate the probability that an animal will survive if kept for a time at a temperature within the lethal zone. This may determine the chance that this animal could cross a region which is so hot that a long exposure would kill it, or that it could survive a snap freeze that was not too prolonged.

Young spring salmon *Oncorhynchus tschawytscha* can live indefinitely in water at 24°C, but die if the temperature is raised by even one half of one degree. To estimate the chance that a fish, swimming in water warmer than 24°C, would survive for a specified period, Brett (1952) placed samples of ten young salmon in tanks in which the water was maintained at a series of constant temperatures and noted the time when each fish died. The results are shown in Figure 6, and it is clear that at the lowest temperature the fish lived on the average longer than at the highest and that the fish varied in the time they remained alive; this is particularly so at the lowest temperature, and is the reason why the line slopes more gradually at that temperature. Brett used only 10 fish in each of these experiments; had he used a larger number of fish in each tank, we might expect that they would have included fish that were both more tolerant and less tolerant of high temperatures than the ones in the original sample. But, provided the original sample was representative of the species as a whole, we should expect the average tolerance to remain much the same as before. So with a larger sample we might expect to find the curve drawn through the observed points looking like the one that is drawn as a broken line in Figure 6. The first fish

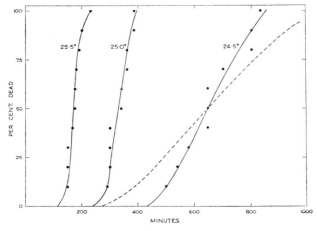

Figure 6

Survival curves from samples of ten young salmon at three different temperatures. The broken line represents an imaginary experiment at 24·5°C, using a much larger sample of fish. Data from Brett (1952).

would die earlier and the last fish later than in Brett's experiment, but the time at which half the fish were dead would remain the same. When one is estimating the time of survival under adverse conditions it is best to estimate the exposure required to kill just half the sample, as this is not influenced by the size of the sample. Also the time required to kill half the sample can be estimated with greater precision than can the time required to kill any other proportion of the animals (Finney, 1947).

4.12 *The influence of temperature within the favourable range on the speed of development*

The fly *Drosophila melanogaster* develops more rapidly at higher temperatures than at low, and in Figure 7 are shown the results of a typical experiment designed to determine precisely the speed of development at a series of carefully controlled constant temperatures. A large number of newly laid eggs was placed at each temperature and the time, t, that elapsed before each one hatched was recorded. The results are in hours, but we can express them as a speed of development by taking the reciprocal, $1/t$. If this is then multiplied by 100 to make it a whole number, $100/t$, we can consider this as a measure of the percentage of the

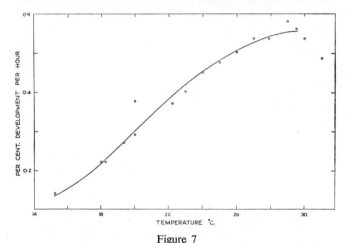

Figure 7

Rate of development of *Drosophila melanogaster* from egg to adult at different constant temperatures. Data from Browning (1952).

developmental period completed in one hour. These are the results that are plotted against temperature in Figure 7. The speed of development becomes proportionally greater at higher temperatures up to a certain point, and then the rate of increase in the speed of development falls off, until at the very highest temperatures the speed of development itself actually begins to fall. This is evidence that this point is within the range of lethal high temperatures for *Drosophila*. Figure 7 also shows the results of measuring the speed of development from egg to adult, and from it we can calculate that *Drosophila* could complete more than three generations in a month at a temperature of 29°C but only one at a temperature of 15°C. The rate at which a population of *Drosophila* could increase at 29°C would thus be much greater than at 15°C.

4.13 *The influence of temperature within the favourable range on length of life and fecundity*

Vance (1949) studied the length of life and the number of eggs laid by the moth *Pyrausta nubilalis* at a series of constant temperatures, and the results he obtained are shown in Table 7. The average length of life decreased at higher temperatures, but the number of eggs produced increased up to 29°C and decreased at 32°C. This is evidence that the decreasing length of life was not due to any lethal influence of temperature *per se* but rather that the moths were living at a faster rate and growing senile sooner at the higher temperature. However, it is likely that at 32°C temperature was having some direct lethal effect, as the number of eggs produced was low and there was a higher proportion of infertile eggs.

Table 7

Influence of constant temperature on longevity and fecundity of female *Pyrausta* kept at 96% RH

Temperature in °C	Mean life span in days	Mean eggs per moth	Proportion infertile per cent
21	15·9	708	1·7
27	14·0	758	1·2
29	10·8	823	0·4
32	8·8	533	5·7

These results were obtained when the relative humidity of the air remained constant. But moisture is an important component of weather for many animals, influencing their chances of survival and reproduction, and we must now consider it in more detail.

4.2

MOISTURE

It is often difficult to measure the moisture component of weather in the environment of an animal.[1] The presence of free water in the form of minute droplets, or absorbed in hygroscopic material

1. A contrasting statement is to be found in Dice (1952), p. 102, the contrast stemming from the considerable difference between the approach taken by community ecologists and that taken here.

like dry grass, may not be apparent and special care may be required in collecting it in order to make a precise estimate of the amount available. The measurement of the amount of water vapour in the air in small confined spaces is a notoriously difficult problem. Solomon (1951) described the use of small pieces of tissue-paper impregnated with cobalt thiocyanate, a substance which changes colour from pink to blue as the humidity increases. Madge (1956) used this method to estimate the relative humidity in the burrows of the underground grass-grub *Oncopera fasciculata*. He found that the air at the bottom of the burrow remained above 90% RH even when the air at the surface of the ground was as low as 40% to 50% RH. Edney (1953) used small electrical hygrometers to estimate the moisture in the air in the places where wood-lice live. On a warm, sunny day when the relative humidity of the air just above a stony shingle was 70% RH, the air in the spaces between the stones where the wood-lice lived was nearly saturated with water vapour. In both these cases conclusions about the ecology of the animals based on measurements of humidity in the open air would have been quite misleading.

4.21 *Loss and gain of water by animals*

Animals lose water from their bodies in a variety of ways. Urine usually contains much water, and faeces are usually damp. The air that an animal exhales while breathing is often more humid than the air it inhales, and so there is a net loss of water. Sweat is mostly water, and many animals lose water by evaporation through the external membranes when the humidity of the air is low. Aquatic animals may lose water by osmosis when the concentration of salts in the water is greater than that in their own body fluids. Most animals can tolerate a certain loss of water from their bodies provided this can be made good later by imbibing water from their surroundings. Water is taken in by drinking or, what amounts to the same thing, eating food which contains a high proportion of water. Some animals, like *Ixodes*, can absorb water from the water vapour of the air, and in aquatic animals, especially those living in fresh streams and ponds, water may enter the body through the 'skin' by osmosis, because the osmotic pressure of their blood is always greater than fresh water.

These are physiological matters and are dealt with in detail in the text-books of general physiology. We will not discuss them further here but will consider a few examples of the way in which moisture influences survival and reproduction in animals.

Loss of water

When the eggs of the Australian field-cricket *Acheta commodus* were kept in containers in which the relative humidity of the air was carefully regulated, all the eggs lost water. Even those in the containers where the humidity was kept as near 100 % as possible

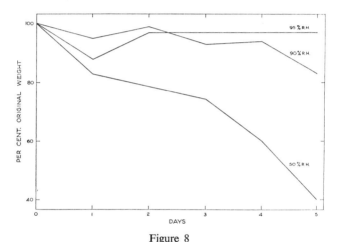

Figure 8

Changes in weight of individual ticks kept at different constant relative humidities. After Lees (1946).

lost weight, and the rate at which the water was lost was greater the lower the humidity. In all cases the eggs died before completing their development. Lees (1946) showed that the rate of loss of water from female sheep-ticks *Ixodes ricinus* was high at low humidities, but that at 95 % RH the ticks did not lose water, their weight remaining fairly steady (Figure 8). In ticks and some other animals there is an 'equilibrium humidity' at which water is neither lost nor gained.

In a study on several species of rodent, the animals were fed on pearled barley whose water content was known, and they were denied water for drinking. Figure 9 shows that hamsters and white rats lost weight quite rapidly when the humidity was 90% RH, whereas kangaroo rats *Dipodomys merriame* lost weight only at low humidities.

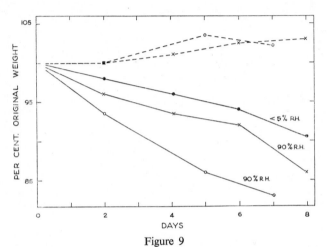

Figure 9

The continuous lines represent changes in weight of kangaroo rats (closed circles), hamsters (open circles) and white rats (crosses), at constant relative humidities when no drinking water was available. The controls (broken lines) show the changes in weight of hamsters and white rats when drinking water was provided. Data from B. Schmidt-Nielsen and K. Schmidt-Nielsen (1951).

Uptake of water

When the eggs of *Acheta commodus* were kept in contact with liquid water, the embryos developed and eventually hatched after a period which depended on the temperature. After two days at 27°C the weight of the egg increased rapidly as a result of water being absorbed by the egg; the weight of water taken up was about equal to the original weight of the egg. About 12 hours

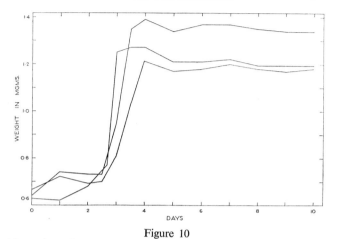

Figure 10

Absorption of water by individual eggs of *Acheta commodus* when incubated in contact with liquid water.

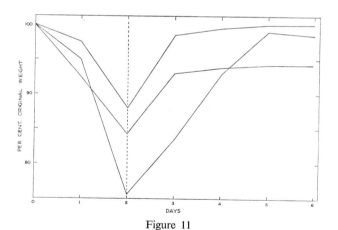

Figure 11

Changes in weight of individual sheep-ticks when kept first at a low humidity, and then at 95% R.H. The dotted line indicates the time when the ticks were placed in humid air. After Lees (1946).

after the weight began to increase, the final weight was attained (Figure 10). The eggs of many other insects behave in a similar way; all eggs that have so far been studied absorb water only from liquid water in contact with the shell. The sheep-tick, on the other hand, can absorb water in appreciable amounts from water vapour in the air, provided the humidity of the air is greater than the 'equilibrium humidity'. Figure 11 shows the results of some of Lees' experiments in which ticks which had lost some water while living at a low humidity were placed in air with a relative humidity of 95 %. The resulting increase in weight was rapid and the water absorbed was retained.

When *Dipodomys* was kept in cages whose relative humidity was greater than about 20 %, the animals increased in weight.

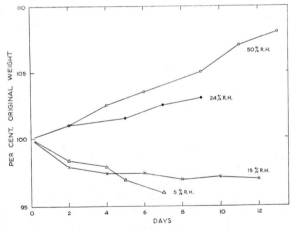

Figure 12

Changes in weight of kangaroo rats kept at different relative humidities without access to drinking-water, but with access to food (cf. Fig. 9). Data from B. Schmidt-Nielsen and K. Schmidt-Nielsen (1951).

Unlike the eggs of *Acheta* and the female *Ixodes*, *Dipodomys* had access to food during these experiments, although it was denied drinking-water. In this case the precise amounts of water taken in with the food was measured, and the water lost in the faeces and urine, and by evaporation, was also measured. Only at humidities below about 10% to 15% RH did the output of water exceed the intake, and under these conditions some two-thirds of the water lost was by evaporation (Figure 12).

There are a few reports of animals that were dried out to constant weight in desiccators at 0% RH and yet became active when they again had access to moisture. The larva of the chironomid fly *Polypedilum vanderplanki* is one of these (Hinton, 1951), but most animals die when they lose a relatively small proportion of the water in their bodies. Their chances of survival will then depend on the humidity of the air around them and on the time for which they are exposed to dryness.

4.3

INTERACTION BETWEEN TEMPERATURE AND MOISTURE

In Sections 4.1 and 4.2 we considered the influence of temperature and moisture on an animal's chances of surviving and reproducing, and we have kept these two influences quite separate. But it is commonly observed that the influence of temperature on an animal depends greatly on the humidity to which it is exposed at the time. Birch (1945) placed eggs of the grain-beetle *Rhizopertha dominica* on grain which had been carefully brought to a known moisture-content and observed the proportion of grubs that died before they reached the end of the first instar. He showed that the mortality depended on both temperature and moisture; at a particular temperature the mortality varied with the moisture content of the grain, and at a particular moisture content mortality varied with the temperature. This complex relationship influencing mortality, known as the *interaction* between temperature and moisture, is shown in the form of a solid diagram in Figure 13.

4.4

OTHER ASPECTS OF WEATHER

There is not space enough in this little book to consider in detail all aspects of weather as they relate to the survival and reproduction of animals, neither is it desirable; the student can search out other examples for himself. It has been indicated in some detail

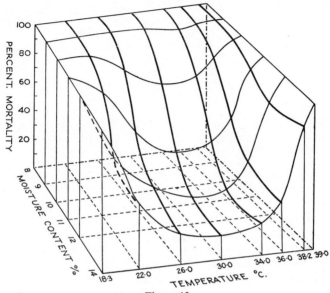

Figure 13

Solid diagram illustrating the interaction between temperature and moisture and effect on mortality of *Rhizopertha dominica*. After Birch (1945).

how two components of weather, temperature and moisture, influence the survival, fecundity and speed of development of some animals. In the rest of this chapter only three other examples will be given, each of which influences the animal in a different way from the others, but all are best thought of as components of the animal's weather.

4.41 *Influence of light on fecundity*

Females of the Queensland fruit-fly *Strumeta tryoni*, if kept in the laboratory in complete darkness, do not lay eggs, but if given as little as two hours' illumination per day produce some eggs. Table 8 shows the results of an experiment in which the length of 'daylight' was increased, and it is clear that under these conditions the fecundity of the females increased.

Table 8

Influence of length of light period on the fecundity of *Strumeta tryoni:* illumination during light period 240 lumens per square foot

Hours of light per day	*Mean number of eggs per female per week*
0	0
2	0·97
4	2·53
7·5	3·52

Barton-Browne (1956) observed that the flies were more active in the light and concluded that this was sufficient to explain the results in Table 8. In darkness the flies were inactive and fed very little, whereas in the light they became active and fed, the amount of food they consumed depending upon the length of the light period.

4.42 *The rate of flow of a stream*

The larvæ of the mosquito *Anopheles minimus* are usually to be found round the shaded edges of pools or streams. If, however, the only shade available is in the middle of the stream, the larvæ move towards the shade, and this occurs whether the stream is flowing or not. In water moving at a speed of less than 0·3 feet per second, Thompson (1951) found that larvæ that swam out towards the middle were able to anchor themselves against the current on blades of grass growing in the water, but in faster flowing water they were swept away and perished. The current strongly influences a larva's chance of survival and is therefore a part of its environment. By analogy with the wind in the environment of a terrestrial animal, the current as experienced by a mosquito larva is best thought of as a part of the weather.

4.43 *Salinity and survival*

Young Atlantic salmon were kept in jars containing mixtures of sea water and river water, and the time that elapsed before half the fish died was measured. In this way Huntsman and Hoar (1939) showed that all the fish survived for 45 hours when the salinity of the water was 10 parts per thousand, whereas in a salinity of 20 parts per thousand the median survival time was about 15 hours, and in a salinity of 28 parts per thousand about

8 hours (the salinity of sea water is about 30 parts per thousand). Here the salinity of the water influenced the chance that a fish would survive in a way that is quite analogous with the humidity of the air in the environment of a terrestrial animal, and it is best, when thinking about the ecology of salmon, to consider salinity as a component of the weather.

In Chapter 3 we saw that resources were an important component of the environment of the sheep-tick, and in the next chapter we shall consider this aspect of environment in more detail.

5

Resources

Food and shelter may influence an animal's chances of surviving and reproducing, not only because the amount of a resource that is available may be either abundant or in short supply, but also because the quality of the resource may vary. In Section 5.1 we shall consider only the quantitative aspects of resources. In Section 5.2 we shall go on to consider the qualitative aspects.

5.1

THE QUANTITATIVE ASPECTS OF RESOURCES

5.11 *Abundance and shortage*

Man grows crops and maintains pastures and forests successfully despite the presence of many herbivorous animals, and it is clear that most herbivores live amid a great abundance of food. On the other hand, it is common enough for locusts to eat all the available food in some local situation. Similarly, with shelter or nesting-sites, we may easily find examples which contrast occasions of abundance with occasions of scarcity. In the hills of northern England there is an abundance of shelter for ticks. On the other hand, gannetries are often reported as being crowded with birds, giving clear evidence of a severe shortage of nesting-places. The shortage of food experienced by the locusts and the shortage of nesting-sites experienced by the gannets is called an *absolute shortage*, because such a large proportion of the stocks of the resource are used up that some animals do not get enough.

This condition may be contrasted with the shortage of food experienced by the sheep-tick. The tick is always surrounded by food, in the form of blood, which is more than enough for its needs, yet we saw in section 1.56 that many ticks die each year of starvation because the food is inaccessible; the ticks cannot find it. This kind of shortage, which is common in nature, is called a *relative shortage* of a resource. In the next sections we shall consider these two kinds of shortage in more detail.

5.12 *Absolute shortage*

Leopold (1943) described what happened to a population of mule deer *Odocoileus hemionus* on the Kaibab plateau in Arizona, when most of the mountain-lions and wolves that preyed on them were shot. The deer multiplied enormously in numbers until they had eaten most of the bush and herbage which was their food. Then many deer died of starvation without reproducing. During the period when the numbers were increasing, the deer were so numerous relative to their supplies of food that they trampled and broke many of the plants so that they did not regenerate (Rasmussen, 1941). The result was that food remained scarce even after the numbers of deer had decreased. This example illustrates a number of ways in which absolute shortages may influence the numbers of animals in a population. First, starvation killed many deer before they could reproduce, and so the size of the next generation was reduced. Also some of their food did not regenerate, which meant that there was less food available for the next generation. When we are considering the influence of absolute shortages on any population of animals we must always take into account these two effects: the influence on the numbers in the next generation, and the influence on the amount of the resource that will be available for them. In the next three examples we shall see that populations do not always respond to an absolute shortage in the same way as deer, neither are future supplies of resource always influenced by dense populations using them, in the same way as food for deer.

In Australia the blowfly *Lucilia sericata* lays its eggs on carrion. Often the numbers of maggots that hatch are so great that there is not enough food to go round, and many of them starve. For example, Waterhouse (1947) set out the carcases of 27 sheep in the field and allowed wild flies to lay eggs on them freely. A carcase of the size he used could have produced as many as

80,000 flies, on the average, provided only about 80,000 eggs had been laid on it. But in fact so many eggs were laid that the absolute shortage of food was extreme, and most of the larvæ died of starvation; the average number of flies that emerged from each carcase was only 10,000. There can be no doubt that crowding had reduced the number of flies in the next generation.

The supply of food for maggots depends on the number and size of carcases in the area. This is determined by the number of sheep and other suitable animals that die, and is quite independent of the crowding of maggots in the last generation. Blowflies are like deer in that the absolute shortage of food in one generation determines the numbers of the next generation. But food for blowflies is unlike food for deer, because the amount available for one generation is not influenced by the shortage experienced by the previous generation.

In both *Lucilia* and deer some food is eaten by individuals that are destined to starve before they reproduce, and from the point of view of the population this food is wasted. It is useful to distinguish between this and 'effective' food, that is, food which is used to produce the next generation.

The wasp *Microphanurus basalis* lays its eggs in the eggs of the bug *Nezara viridula*. As a rule *Microphanurus* will not lay in an egg that already contains an egg or larva of one of its own kind, but even if it does, only one larva will survive, because the other is eaten along with the contents of the egg. This behaviour ensures that no matter how few eggs of *Nezara* there may be relative to the numbers of *Microphanurus*, that is, no matter how great the absolute shortage of food may be for *Microphanurus*, none will be wasted on individuals that do not get enough to complete their life cycles. So the numbers of *Microphanurus* in the next generation are not influenced by the absolute shortage experienced by their parents, but only by the number of eggs of *Nezara*, that is, the amount of food that was available. In this respect *Microphanurus* is quite different from both deer and blowflies. But food for *Microphanurus* is like food for the deer, in that the number of *Nezara* that survive to lay eggs, and so provide food for the next generation, depends on the numbers of *Microphanurus* in the previous generation. The greater this number is, relative to the number of eggs, the fewer *Nezara* will survive.

Kluijver (1951) studied two populations of birds, the great tit *Parus major*, one living in a woodland of old trees, and one in a woodland of young trees, and found that the population was denser in the old trees. He attributed this to the fact that the old trees had more holes in them suitable for *Parus* to make nests in. In both cases nearly all the holes were used, so it is likely that at the beginning of the breeding season the tits in the young trees experienced an absolute shortage of nesting-holes. Once a pair had established a nest, the birds' behaviour ensured that they had the unrestricted use of it during the season, so that any hole that was used at all was used to rear progeny for the next generation. *Parus* thus resembles *Microphanurus* in that the numbers in the next generation do not depend on the absolute shortage of a resource experienced by their parents, but only on the amount of that resource available. But because nesting sites are not destroyed by being used, the amount of this resource available to the next generation is not influenced by the numbers of birds that sought to use it in the last generation. It thus resembles food for *Lucilia*, and differs from food for both deer and *Microphanurus*.

These four examples illustrate what is likely to be the result when a population of animals becomes crowded relative to its supplies of some resource. The numbers of animals in the next generation may be reduced because of the shortage (deer and blowflies), or the next generation may be just as numerous as it would have been had there been just enough of the resource to go round (*Microphanurus* and tits). At the same time, the amount of the resource that will be available for the next generation may be reduced as a result of the crowding in the previous generation (deer and *Microphanurus*), or it may be quite unaffected, as in the blowflies and tits.

5.13 *Relative shortage*

The small island of Berlenga supported a population of rabbits until some cats were introduced to prey on them (Elton, 1927). The cats increased in numbers until they had eaten all the rabbits, and then the cats all died of starvation. The island is small and neither the rabbits nor the cats could escape from it.

The progress of events as the numbers of deer on the Kaibab plateau increased was different. The food available decreased, but it was not entirely destroyed. Some areas were completely denuded and did not regenerate but others, that were by chance not quite so heavily grazed and trampled, or were better able to stand the grazing and trampling, persisted. Thus the food, having been plentiful and widespread, became scarce and patchily distributed. After most of the deer had died the population came to be restricted, not so much by the absolute amount of food in the area as by its distribution: it had become hard to find.

The difference between these two situations is to be explained by the nature of the area of distribution of the two populations relative to the ability of the animals to roam in search of food. The island of Berlenga is small and uniform and the cats could easily roam all over it in search of a meal. The Kaibab plateau, on the other hand, is large and heterogeneous in its terrain, and a deer would not have time to search more than a small proportion of it unsuccessfully before starving to death. In the event, small colonies of deer feed on the patches of food until they have depleted them and then must move on in search of a new supply. But mule-deer seem extremely 'reluctant' to move from the place where they have been feeding. Some do and are successful, but many perish. It is the ability to disperse that permits the population of deer to maintain itself. But the patchy distribution of food, relative to the poor powers of dispersal of the deer, ensures that some food goes undiscovered and therefore unused, even though some of the animals do not get enough to eat.

Another example of this same situation is the case of the lady-bird beetle *Rodolia cardinalis*, which was imported from Australia to California late in the nineteenth century, as a predator of the scale-insect *Icerya purchasi*. At that time *Icerya* was so abundant on the citrus trees that the industry was threatened with destruction. When it was released in the citrus groves, *Rodolia* found itself surrounded with an abundance of food, and it increased rapidly in numbers and destroyed most of the *Icerya*. As a result, the distribution of *Icerya* changed in a way quite similar to the bushes that the deer fed on. It became rare and patchily distributed. Small colonies of the scale would multiply for a while until they were found by *Rodolia*, which would destroy them completely. But meanwhile, larvæ of the scale had migrated to found new colonies that would also thrive for a time and then be destroyed. There is a sparse population of *Icerya* still living in

California, because the ladybirds have not yet happened to destroy all the local colonies simultaneously, as the cats did to the rabbits on the small and homogeneous island of Berlenga.

Many examples similar to these two are known and they lead to the conclusion that where the powers of dispersal of the feeding animals are great relative to those of their food, both feeders and food are likely to be rare and patchily distributed, whereas where the powers of dispersal of the feeders are poor relative to those of their food, much food will go undiscovered, and the animals, although they may be numerous locally, will be rare and very patchily distributed.

In both cases just discussed the relative shortage of food arose as a result of a change in the distribution of the food, and this change was brought about as the result of the large numbers of animals feeding. The population began amid an abundance of food and increased to the point where the animals experienced a severe absolute shortage, and many died. The remainder were then faced with a relative shortage because the food that was left had become hard to find. This situation is common in nature and a number of examples may be found in Elton (1958). But relative shortages do not always arise through the activities of the feeding animals, as the following examples will show.

There are a large number of insects that lay their eggs into the bodies of other insects. The eggs hatch and the larva grows to maturity on the contents of the 'host's' body, killing the host in the process. *Anarhopus sydneyensis* is such an insect which 'parisitises' the mealybug *Pseudococcus adonidum*. *Anarhopus* must search out mealybugs, and if they are sparsely distributed her chance of finding one may be quite small. She thus experiences a relative shortage of food. But if *Anarhopus* finds a mealybug, the larva that hatches from her egg is sure to have enough food to complete its life cycle. This is unlike the deer or *Rodolia*. But like them the feeding of *Anarhopus* reduces the food available for the next generation.

The chance that *Ixodes* will find a meal depends on the number of sheep and other warm-blooded animals in its vicinity, as was shown in section 1.54, and this depends on many things, but not on the number of *Ixodes* seeking a meal.

The tsetse-fly *Glossina morsitans* sucks blood chiefly from the larger species of antelope in Africa. It requires to feed frequently but does not stay near its food between meals. So each meal is preceded by an independent search. If antelopes are sparsely distributed, a fly may have little chance of finding enough food to produce many, or any, offspring, despite the fact that the amount of blood in one antelope is sufficient to feed many flies. Potts and Jackson (1952) demonstrated this when they exterminated a population of tsetse-flies from a large area by shooting most, but by no means all, the antelopes living in the area. Changes in the number of antelopes occur independently of the number of tsetse-flies feeding on them, but they nevertheless determine the chances of survival and reproduction of the flies.

Ixodes and *Glossina* are like *Anarhopus* in that each meal must be preceded by an independent search in which there is a chance that no food will be found, but unlike *Anarhopus* they do not influence the amount of food available for future generations. These three species are also alike in that the relative shortage is not the result of a change in the distribution of their food, brought about by their own feeding; it happens because their food is distributed from the first in discrete units, each one of which, when found, represents enough food for one stage in their lives.

The last example of a relative shortage is perhaps the antithesis of the other examples. The mosquito larva living in a pond and feeding on minute particles of food suspended in the water may not be able to get enough to eat, simply because the food is too dilute. There may be plenty of food in the pond for many larvæ, were it concentrated, but the larva is limited by the amount of water it can strain with its 'feeding brushes', and even though it feeds continuously it may starve. Again the amount of food available may be independent of the number of larvæ feeding on it.

5.14 *The relationship between no shortage, absolute shortage and relative shortage*

When the deer on the Kaibab plateau were being preyed upon by mountain-lions there was no shortage of food for them. After the mountain-lions had been shot, the number of deer increased; they experienced a severe absolute shortage of food and many of them died. But their feeding had altered the distribution of their food. It had become so patchily distributed that a state of relative shortage developed, which persisted. This sequence of events, from no shortage through absolute shortage to relative shortage of some resource, is commonly observed in nature and frequently results when, for some reason, a population which has not been dense enough to use up a high proportion of its resources multiplies to the point where it does.

There are some animals, like the blowfly *Lucilia* and the tit *Parus*, whose populations are so dense relative to their resources that there are usually more than enough animals in each generation to use up all the resource. These animals, in which the supply of a resource for one generation does not depend on the density of the previous generation, seem to be able to exist as extensive natural populations at densities that ensure a persistent absolute shortage of the resource.

Animals like the sheep-tick and the tsetse-fly, which also belong to the group in which the supply of a resource for one generation does not depend on the density of the previous generation, but in which the powers of dispersal are poor relative to those of their food, seem always to exist in a state of more or less severe relative shortage. It is difficult to imagine either of these species being so well supplied with food as always to get enough. At the same time they can surely never consume so much of their food that they experience an absolute shortage.

5.2

THE QUALITATIVE ASPECTS OF RESOURCES

So far we have considered food and other resources as varying only in amount and in distribution, but clearly the quality of the resource may also influence an animal's chances of surviving and reproducing. For example, the aphid *Aphis fabae* feeds on the sap of the spindle tree *Euonymus europaeus*. Kennedy and Booth (1951) confined adult aphids on young, mature and senescent leaves, and found that they produced fewer offspring when they fed on mature leaves than when they fed on the other kinds. Sheep in southern Australia grazing on pastures that are growing on soil deficient in cobalt have a much reduced chance of survival compared with sheep that have cobalt added to their diet. That food can vary in quality, and that this can influence the chances of surviving and reproducing is too well known to need any further examples here.

Resources other than food also vary in quality, and we shall consider a few examples of how this may influence the numbers of animals in a population.

The grey-lag goose builds a flat nest on the ground, and occasionally an egg will roll out of the nest. When this happens the goose usually retrieves it by rolling it back into the nest with the underside of its bill. Sometimes, however, the egg rolls away and is lost (Lorentz and Tinbergen, 1938). Now the nature of the nesting site, whether it be on top of a steep knoll or on flat ground, will influence the chance that an egg, having rolled out of the nest, will be retrieved.

The cricket *Acheta commodus* will readily lay eggs in either sand or stiff black clay, provided it is moist (Browning, 1954). If the soil remains moist, the eggs will develop and the larvæ will hatch in both soils. But the amount of water held in a clay soil when it is saturated is much greater than the amount held in saturated sand; so in dry weather the sand will dry out to the point where the eggs are killed by desiccation more rapidly than will clay under similar conditions. The chances of survival of the eggs of *Acheta* thus depend on the quality of the soil that the females use as places in which to lay their eggs, and also on the weather.

In the case of the goose, the influence of the quality of the site on the chances of survival of the eggs seemed to be quite independent of any other component of environment, but in the case of *Acheta* the quality of the resource only became important through the influence of the weather. It would seem that the quality of resources other than food usually exerts its influence on animals as a result of an interaction with some other component of environment. I have not been able to find well documented examples, but it is easy to see that a tit may have a greater chance of survival in the presence of predators or during a severe winter if the hole where it builds its nest is deep rather than shallow. In the absence of an interaction with predators or with the weather it may make little difference what sort of a hole the tit chooses.

However, when we were considering the qualitative aspects of food at the beginning of this section, we did not take into account any interactions with other components of environment, and it does seem that, unlike other resources, the influence of food is usually independent of the rest of the environment. (Which is not to say that other components have *no* influence, but simply that if they do their influence is usually so slight that we can afford to ignore it.) An animal requires the same kind of food irrespective of the presence or absence of predators in its environment, or of the presence of large or small numbers of its own kind. But on the other hand, there is sometimes an inter-action with weather; it is well known that the kinds of food that are most suitable for man in the winter differ considerably from those most suitable in summer. So although interactions between the quality of food and other components of environment are usually unimportant, we should nevertheless expect to find some cases in which they had some measurable influence on an animal's chances of survival and reproduction.

6

Members of the Same Species

In Chapter 5 animals were considered as being crowded when the density of the population was great relative to their stocks of food or some other resource. But even when there is plenty of food and shelter for all of them, the animals in a dense population may interfere with one another in some way and so reduce each other's chances of survival and reproduction. This sort of crowding might be discussed as a shortage of living room, in which case living room might properly be considered as a resource, and included in Chapter 5 along with other sorts of resources. But living room has a number of qualities which seem to exclude it from the category of resources: for example, resources may never be thought of as reducing an animal's chances of survival and reproduction by being too plentiful. There are many situations in nature, however, where there may be too much living room, but only in the sense that an animal may have too few of its own kind near it. For this reason I think we are likely to get muddled if we try to talk about 'not enough living room'; it is more fruitful to discuss this sort of crowding in terms of 'too many animals of the same kind'. This chapter will be concerned first with the problems of crowding and then, in section 6.2, with the problems of underpopulation, as they relate to the chances of survival and reproduction of individuals in a population.

6.1

CROWDING

6.11 *The influence of crowding on fecundity*

Birch, Park and Frank (1951) studied the influence of crowding on the fecundity of the flour-beetle *Tribolium confusum*. Various numbers of beetles were put in tubes, each containing eight grams of flour and yeast. The tubes were kept at 29°C and 70% RH. Each week for four weeks the flour was renewed, the old flour being sifted and the number of eggs counted. There were fifteen tubes with one pair of beetles each, a male and a female, fifteen with eight pairs, fifteen with forty pairs and fifteen with eighty pairs. Figure 14 shows the results they obtained; the beetles laid fewer eggs in the presence of large numbers of their own kind than they did when there were few other beetles in the jars with them. These beetles eat their own eggs, and proportionately more eggs are eaten when the population is dense than when it is sparse. Cannibalism of this kind accounted for some of the reduction in fecundity that was observed. (Fecundity was measured by counting the number of eggs that were present at the end of each week and dividing by the number of female beetles. This is not necessarily the same as the number of eggs laid per female per week.) But even

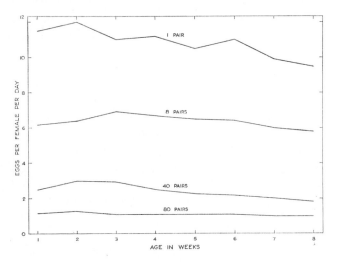

Figure 14

Numbers of eggs found at the end of each week in tubes containing varying numbers of adults of *Tribolium confusum.* After Birch, Park and Frank (1951).

when cannibalism was taken into account, there was still a considerable fall in fecundity owing to the direct effects of crowding. How crowding exerts its influence on the number of eggs laid by the females is not known.

Southwick (1958) studied populations of house-mice *Mus musculus* living in corn-ricks in England. The ricks were built of sheaves of wheat or oats and there seemed to be ample food and shelter for all the mice in all the ricks. In some of the ricks the population of mice was sparse, and in others it was dense – over 1600 mice per cubic metre. Table 9 shows that the proportion of females that were pregnant in the sparse populations when the counts were made was greater than the proportion pregnant in the denser populations, and that in the sparse populations the mice had larger litters.

Table 9

Influence of density of population of mice on proportion of females pregnant and on number of young produced

Population:	*Sparse*	*Medium*	*Dense*	*Very dense*
Average no. per m^3	34	118	340	1600
Average percentage pregnant	58	50	51	43
Average young per litter	6·2	5·7	5·6	5·1

However, even in the densest populations the number of young produced was sufficient to cause the population to continue to increase in numbers. Nowhere were the mice so numerous that they consumed a large proportion of the food that was available, nor was shelter limiting, and the weather can be taken as having been the same for all. There were few predators, and there was little disease.

There seems to be nothing else about a dense population that reduces the likelihood of a mouse becoming pregnant other than the sheer weight of numbers; and we can only conclude that in some way, as yet not fully understood, a mouse living in a dense population is less likely to become pregnant than one that has fewer of its own kind about it. The house-mouse and the flour-beetle are only two of the many species in which crowding is known to reduce fecundity. In neither the mouse nor the beetle do we know how this phenomenon comes about, but in the case of the voles discussed in the next section, the underlying causes have been examined in some detail.

6.12 *A complex example illustrating the influence of crowding on fecundity and survival*

Chitty (1952) studied a number of populations of voles *Microtus agrestis*, in an area near Lake Vyrnwy in Wales, and found that the numbers in each population increased over a period of a few years to a maximum and then fell rapidly. A low birth-rate and a low survival-rate, especially among the young, were the main causes of the decline, which lasted for two generations. But by the third generation the birth-rate was rising and the survival-rate was also high, so the population began to increase again. This sequence of events occurred in several populations, but the peak was reached, and the decline arrested, in different years in different populations. Chitty could find no component of environment that would account for his observations except the large numbers in the generation preceding the decline. Food and shelter were adequate, the weather was the same for all populations whether they were increasing or decreasing, and predators and disease seemed not to be any more important in one year than in another. He noticed, however, that when voles are numerous they meet one another frequently in the runways that they construct in the grass, and when they meet they fight. He postulated that the fighting might have some physiological effect that could be transmitted through several generations.

Clarke (1953) showed that when voles were kept crowded in a cage they fought constantly, but the fighting seldom ended in the death of one of the fighters. He went on to show that certain endocrine glands, notably the thymus, spleen and adrenal glands, became enlarged in crowded animals compared with those kept in uncrowded cages. And Dawson (1956) showed that haemolytic anaemia was associated with the enlargement of the spleen. More recently Chitty (1957) has produced evidence that some form of hereditary mechanism is operating in these animals that maintains the pathological conditions in the population. The complete explanation is as yet far from clear, but there is no doubt that crowded voles, because of the constant fighting that occurs in dense populations, produce fewer offspring, that their offspring are more likely to die before they are weaned, and that those that survive also produce fewer offspring than would be expected in a now sparse population. It was this latter fact that caused the numbers in the population to decline through two generations, even though their numbers at the end of the first generation were lower than they had been in the year before they had increased to their maximum density.

Flour-beetles, mice and voles are three examples of the way in which the speed at which a population increases may change as a result simply of the crowding that accompanies an increase in numbers.

In voles the population began to decline long before all the resources had been used up, and when all other components of environment seemed to favour further increase. There is thus a kind of built-in mechanism in voles that ensures that the density of the population does not go above certain levels. This has been called a *self-regulatory mechanism*. Self-regulatory mechanisms are attracting a good deal of attention from population ecologists at the present time, and they are being found to be rather widespread in populations among the vertebrates.

6.2

UNDERPOPULATION

6.21 *The influence of small numbers on fecundity*

The tsetse-fly *Glossina morsitans* of Africa feeds by sucking blood, which it obtains mainly from antelopes. The female needs to feed a number of times in order to produce one offspring. Potts and Jackson (1952) shot most of the larger antelopes in an area of some 600 square miles at Shinyanga, an operation which took a number of years to complete, and during this time they made regular counts of tsetse-flies in the area. As the number of antelopes decreased, so did the numbers of *Glossina*, until the population of flies was much smaller than it had been before the shooting began. As a routine Potts and Jackson dissected some of the females from each sample to see whether they had sperm in their spermathecae, a sure sign that they had mated. Towards the end of the experiment, when the population had become very sparse, a virgin female was found, the first one that had ever been caught in the wild in all the years of study of tsetse-flies in Africa. The numbers in the population fell still further, and as they did so the proportion of unmated females in the samples rose until virtually no female that was caught was found to have mated. Potts and Jackson attributed this to the sparseness of the population: a female as she emerged from her pupal case was usually too far away from the nearest male for them to have a good chance of meeting. The population was already experiencing a severe relative shortage of food (section 5.2), and in addition the flies were unlikely to find mates because they were so few. The population became extinct over the entire area soon afterwards.

We saw in section 1.56 that *Ixodes* must frequently fail to find a mate because there is no member of the opposite sex on its host. This is especially true when the population is sparse, and Milne found good reason to believe that the spread of ticks from one farm to another is only possible when a large population is introduced to a new area at one time. Only then do the sexes have sufficient chance of meeting.

Elton (1958) wrote a delightful book in which he described a number of cases in which animals had succeeded in crossing major geographic barriers like oceans, mountain ranges or waterfalls, and had become established and numerous in a new region. But there must be untold cases of one or a few individuals successfully crossing such a barrier only to die without reproducing, either because the new population was too small or the individuals too widely dispersed for them to find mates, or because individuals or small groups are unable to survive in the face of some other component of environment.

6.22 *Underpopulation in relation to predators*

The musk-ox *Ovibos moschatus* lives in herds, and when attacked by predators the herd clumps together with the animals on the outside facing outwards toward the enemy. The horns of the musk-ox are large and curved, and the wall of horns which the predator must break through in order to get a meal is like a nineteenth-century British square in the face of the enemy. But if the herd is not large enough this technique of defence is inadequate and the herd is easily broken up. The musk-ox population of Canada was seriously depleted by human predation, against which their defence was quite useless, but their complete extermination became inevitable once the size of the herds had been reduced to a certain level, for then wolves and other predators were able to prey on them more easily (Hone, 1934).

6.23 Underpopulation in relation to weather

There are many ways in which animals modify the severity of the weather, and thereby alter their chances of survival and reproduction. For example, hive-bees *Apis mellifica* may keep the temperature of their hive below the lethal temperature in very hot weather by bringing water to the hive and by keeping the air in circulation with the beating of their wings. But if the numbers of bees in a hive are not great enough they may be unable to reduce the temperature sufficiently, and the whole population may perish.

Sheep in Australia usually feed in groups and in cold, windy weather they usually congregate, packed close together. In most parts of Australia the temperature, even in mid-winter, is not low enough to kill sheep, but in other areas the weather is much more severe. A mob of sheep may survive a blizzard, only the ones on the outside being frozen, provided the mob is large enough, whereas a single sheep or a small group would be killed.

6.24 Underpopulation in relation to a resource

The larvæ of the jack-pine sawfly *Neodiprion banksianae* are usually found feeding in groups on pine-needles. They hatch from eggs laid in pine needles and the groups form near the places where the eggs were laid, though not necessarily on the same needles. Ghent (1960) showed that the death-rate among newly-hatched larvæ was lower when four larvæ were placed together on a young pine-needle than when the larvæ were kept singly (Table 10). In both cases many larvæ died in their first instar without feeding at all, but in the groups a larva that got any food usually survived, whereas among the single individuals about half the larvæ that actually started feeding died before they completed the first instar.

Table 10

Death-rate among young sawfly larvæ reared in groups of four or singly on pine-needles; figures in percentages

	Grouped	Solitary
Died without feeding	44·2	67·2
Died after feeding	10·4	16·4
Survived	45·4	16·4
Total	100·0	100·0

Ghent suggested that the larvæ differed in their ability to break through the cuticle of the pine-needle and begin feeding. Once this had been done by a larva, however, a feeding-site was established which could then be used by as many as seven larvæ at a time. A group of larvæ thus had a chance of including an individual that was capable of breaking the cuticle, whereas a solitary larva either could do this or could not, and if it could not it starved. Table 10 shows that few larvæ, whether solitary or in a group, died once they had begun to feed, the difference between the two lots of larvæ being almost entirely due to those that died without feeding.

This chapter has illustrated some of the ways in which an animal's chances of surviving and reproducing are influenced by its fellows being either too numerous or too few in its vicinity. But other species also form part of an animal's environment, and in the next chapter it will be shown how they, too, may influence the number of animals in a population.

7

Members of Other Species

So far our discussion has been confined to animals, plants only entering the story in so far as they provide food, shelter or some other resource for an animal. Animal ecologists customarily think of plants only in this light, and not uncommonly plant ecologists give the impression that, if they think of animals at all, it is only as a distracting interference in an otherwise orderly universe. But the principles that help in understanding the ways in which animal populations change in numbers and distribution should also be useful in understanding the changes that take place in populations of plants. There will be differences, but we might expect them to be differences in degree rather than in kind. For example, most animals are able to move about freely, and most plants must remain in one spot all their lives. But some animals are sessile and some plants are motile, and every organism, plant or animal, has a means of dispersing at some stage in its life-cycle. This chapter will attempt to show some of the ways in which other species, be they animals, plants or micro-organisms, may influence the density and distribution of the population of animals, plants or micro-organisms that we may be studying.

7.1

OTHER SPECIES THAT INFLUENCE DISPERSAL

In Chapter 1 we saw how the sheep-tick *Ixodes* was unable to move more than a few inches from the place where it fell from its host. The distribution of a population of ticks could expand into a new area only if the ticks were carried there while they were attached to their hosts. And because sheep carried large numbers of ticks relative to the numbers carried by other species of hosts, sheep were the most effective animals in enabling a population of ticks to expand its distribution into nearby favourable grazing land (section 1.56).

Plants may also be dispersed in this way. In South Australia the seeds of the common weed *Echium plantaginium* may often be found tangled in the wool of sheep, and there seems to be little doubt that the sheep is chiefly responsible for the present wide distribution of *Echium*. *Echium* was found first in the north-eastern pastoral district of the state around the beginning of the century. In less than a decade it had spread to the central agricultural district, a distance of several hundred miles. Sheep are plentiful in both areas, and there is much traffic between them. It was not until much later, some time after 1940, that *Echium* appeared in the south-eastern region of the state: at first along stock-routes, and in isolated patches on certain properties where sheep were grazing. Now it is widespread. The first appearance of *Echium* in the south-east coincided with the introduction of many sheep, as the country was developed, following the discovery of the need for certain minerals as fertilisers. Previously this area had been backward and rather isolated, with little traffic in sheep between it and the other regions. *Echium* differs from *Ixodes* in that a few seeds, transported on a single sheep, are enough to establish a permanent and expanding colony if they fall on suitable soil. The speed at which the distribution expands, however, is greatly assisted by sheep transporting the seeds.

Many examples of this kind could be quoted, but perhaps the most important species aiding the dispersal of other species is man. He transports innumerable species – animals, plants and micro-organisms – throughout the world, some of which, like *Echium* and myxoma virus, have readily become established, though many others must have died without becoming established, in much the same way as *Ixodes* does when only a few individuals reach a new area at one time.

Man's activities can also lead to a decrease in the powers of dispersal of animals or plants. For example, sheep on hill grazings are confined to certain areas by fences erected by farmers. It is convenient to consider the fence as an extension of man's

activities; man determines the distribution and numbers of
fences and it is this distribution that influences the dispersal of
Ixodes.

7.2

SPECIES THAT USE OTHER SPECIES AS FOOD

7.21 *Predators*

Predators use animals as food, and kill their prey in order to feed.
The prey is thus a resource for the predator. In Chapter 5 a
number of examples were given of the ecology of predators in
relation to their food, but here we are concerned with the
ecology of a population of prey in the presence of predators.

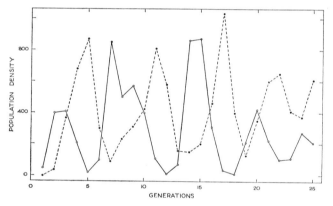

Figure 15

Changes in numbers of the beetle *Callosobruchus chinensis* (solid line)
and its predator *Heterospilus prosopidis* (broken line), reared under
controlled conditions. After Utida (1957).

Utida (1957) described an experiment carried out with a population of weevils *Callosobruchus chinensis* which was preyed upon
by a wasp *Heterospilus prosopidis*. The weevil lives in stored *azuki*
beans in Japan and the wasp lays its eggs in the grubs of the
weevil, and the larva of the wasp eats and kills the grub. Utida
kept the insects in jars in which the food for the weevils was
renewed at regular intervals, and the jars were kept in incubators

where the temperature, humidity and light remained constant. At regular intervals he counted the number of both weevils and wasps. Figure 15 shows the results of one such experiment. The number of animals in both populations fluctuated widely, but the number of wasps always fell behind that of the weevils. The rather even fluctuations that were observed in Utida's experiment may be explained as follows. When the numbers of predators are few, the average chance of survival and reproduction in a population of prey is high, and this leads to an increase in numbers of the prey. But the increase in the numbers of the prey brings about an increase in the chances of survival and reproduction in the population of predators, not only because there is more food, but also because food is easier to find. This leads to an increase in the numbers of predators. The greater number of predators decreases the average chances of survival and reproduction of the prey, and their numbers decline, with a resulting decrease in the numbers of predators. This in turn is followed by an increase in the numbers of prey and the cycle is repeated. Thus an oscillation may be set up which, if nothing else intervenes, may continue indefinitely.

Many ecologists feel that oscillations like those in Utida's experiments would be found in nature where a population was living in the presence of an active predator. But a number of careful studies of natural populations have revealed a rather different pattern of events. It now seems likely that the characteristic oscillations of the laboratory experiments are caused by some feature in the artificial environment created in the laboratory.

The Australian scale-insect *Icerya purchasi* was accidentally introduced into the orange-groves in California towards the end of the nineteenth century. It multiplied rapidly until the insects were abundant in almost every tree, and the citrus industry was threatened with disaster. There were few native insects in California that preyed on *Icerya*, so some ladybirds *Rodolia cardinalis* were imported from Australia and released in the orange groves. The presence of *Rodolia* so reduced the chance of survival of *Icerya* that, where previously it had been increasing rapidly in numbers, it now began to decline. From whole trees and groves the scale was exterminated and the density of the population fell rapidly. But the area over which *Icerya* was distributed remained much as it had been; the individuals were now much further apart. At present *Icerya* occurs as a sparse population spread over a wide area, in which small colonies multiply for a while until they are found by *Rodolia*, when they are usually completely destroyed. *Icerya* continues to exist in the face of an efficient predator, because the young larvæ, just hatched from the egg, are easily transported on the air. They land and found new colonies, from which new emigrants disperse also. The chances of survival and reproduction of *Rodolia* are now much smaller than they were when *Icerya* was abundant, and neither population is able to multiply rapidly. Nevertheless, neither becomes extinct over the whole area because the powers of dispersal of both are great.

On the Kaibab plateau of Arizona a population of about 4000 deer lived in the presence of a number of species of predators (section 5.12). They managed to do this by existing in small, discrete herds, difficult for the predators to find (Leopold, 1943). When many of the predators were killed the chances of survival and reproduction of the deer increased, leading to such a rapid increase in their numbers that they finally ate out and destroyed much of their food supply. Their numbers then fell to a low level and remained there (section 5.12).

There is little in the last two examples that indicates an oscillation in numbers between predator and prey, in the way Utida showed occurred in his laboratory cultures. Indeed, it would be surprising if this were so, for we have already seen that great changes in numbers in a population may result in changes in the amount and distribution of food (as in the deer on the Kaibab, section 5.12), or in changes in the animals themselves (as in the voles, section 6.12). So the environment of an animal after a population has declined will not, as a rule, be similar to the environment before the increase began. Thus we can expect regular oscillations in populations of either predators or prey to be unusual in nature, where the weather is not constant and resources are not renewed at regular intervals.

However, all the examples in this section show that the distribution and numbers of a predatory species influence the chances of survival and reproduction of their prey. The more abundant the predators are, the less will be the prey's chances of survival and reproduction. The way in which a change in the numbers of predators will influence their prey will depend on the powers of dispersal of both predator and prey, and also on the way in which changes in the numbers of prey influence other components of environment. The deer multiplied and in so doing destroyed much of their own food, but *Icerya* had not produced a very profound influence on its food before *Rodolia* was introduced. After the destruction of their predators, the deer were kept at a low density mainly by a relative shortage of food; after the introduction of its predators, *Icerya* was kept at a low density by predators which had great powers of dispersal; *Icerya* was not exterminated because the predators' powers of dispersal, although great, were not great enough for that.

The pitcher-plant *Nepenthes* is a predator on numerous species of small animals, principally insects, which become trapped in its pitcher, drown in the water, and are digested by the enzymes secreted by the glandular cells lining the pitcher (Lloyd, 1942). The more numerous *Nepenthes* becomes, the smaller will be the chances of survival and reproduction of the species of insects that it traps. But because *Nepenthes* contains chlorophyll and is capable of photosynthesis it is not dependent upon animals for its supplies of nutriment, so the extinction of all the prey in its vicinity would not necessarily lead to the extinction of *Nepenthes*, as would be the case with animal predators (Figure 15).

The ant-lion *Myrmelion formicarius* is the larva of a neuropteran insect. It makes funnel-shaped pits in soft sand and hides beneath the sand in one side of the pit (Wheeler, 1930). When an ant or other small insect falls into the pit the ant-lion rushes out from beneath the sand, seizes the prey, drags it under the sand and sucks the juices from it by means of its specially modified mandibles. Ecologically the ant-lion and its pit are very similar to *Nepenthes* and its pitcher, except that the survival of a population of ant-lions is completely dependent upon the presence of a sufficient number of ants.

7.22 Non-predators

Sheep on hill farms are fed upon by *Ixodes*, and antelopes in Africa are used as food by tsetse-flies. Neither *Ixodes* nor *Glossina* are called predators, because they do not kill their food as they feed. Only when the numbers of feeding animals become very great are the chances of survival of sheep or antelopes significantly reduced. Nevertheless, the ideas we have used in explaining the influence that a population of predators may have on a population of prey apply to these species, too. The chances of survival of sheep and antelopes are only rarely significantly reduced as a result of being fed upon. In both cases this is largely due to their great powers of dispersal relative to those of ticks and tsetse-flies. This ensures that the ticks and tsetse-flies are kept rare relative to the amount of food available. But an increase in the numbers of sheep would increase the chance of survival of ticks, or a decrease in the numbers of antelopes would reduce the chances of survival of tsetse-flies, as it did at Shinyanga (section 5.13).

The influence of ticks on sheep or of tsetse-flies on antelopes is similar to the influence of sheep on the grass or antelopes on the bushes on which they feed. The chances of survival of grass and bushes is influenced only to a slight degree by grazing, until the density of the animals becomes very great. When this happens the plants are killed and the animals starve, but the death of the animals does not always lead to an increase in the numbers of the plants. At least in the case of the plants on the Kaibab plateau, after the deer which fed on them became much fewer than they had been, another component of their environment, the soil, had been so altered as a result of the upsurge in the numbers of the deer that the plants came to experience a relative shortage of suitable places in which to grow, and this resulted in a permanent change in both the numbers and the distribution of the plants.

The presence of the mistletoe, a parasitic plant, influences the chance of survival of the mulga tree *Acacia aneura* in arid Australia, in much the same way as a blood-sucking insect influences the chance of survival of an ungulate. And a rabbit will influence the chance of survival of a young mulga seedling in much the same way as a fox will influence the chance of survival of a rabbit. In all these cases the numbers of the population of feeding species (mistletoe, insect, rabbit and fox) depend greatly on the numbers and distribution of the food (mulga, ungulate, mulga and rabbit). Mistletoe can experience a relative shortage of 'food' in a way that is closely analogous to the relative shortage experienced by *Ixodes* (section 5.13).

7.3

SPECIES THAT SHARE THE SAME RESOURCE

Birch (1953) kept populations of two species of grain beetles *Calandra oryzae* and *Rhizopertha dominica* living together in 12 grams of wheat. The jars containing the beetles were kept at constant temperatures of 29°C and 32°C, and the moisture content of the grain was kept constant. Fifteen identical jars containing a pair of adults of each species were set up at each temperature. Each fortnight the grain was sifted and replenished, and each month the beetles were counted. In all the jars both species increased at first, but at 32°C the populations of *Calandra* dwindled to zero after an average of 37 weeks. At 29°C, however, it was *Rhizopertha* that became extinct, but the average time that elapsed before this happened was much longer. In fact, the

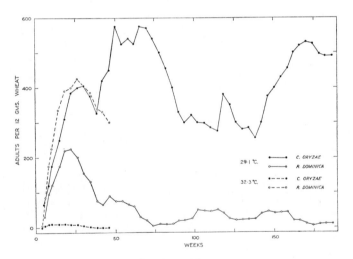

Figure 16

Changes in numbers of *Calandra oryzae* and *Rhizopertha dominica* when cultured together at different temperatures. At 32°C *R. dominica* had the higher finite rate of increase and *C. oryzea* rapidly became extinct, whereas at 29°C *C. oryzea* had the higher finite rate of increase and *R. dominica* eventually became extinct. After Birch (1953).

population that survived for the shortest time died out in 38 weeks and there were still a few *Rhizopertha* left in 8 out of the 15 jars after 190 weeks, when the experiment stopped. Figure 16 shows these results. At both temperatures the beetles persisted indefinitely when only one species was present in a jar, and under these circumstances the numbers were greater than they were when two species lived together. Table 11 sets out some of the details of the experiment and includes the finite rate of increase of each species. This is the rate at which each species multiplies during the early stages of growth of the population, when living alone under the specified conditions of temperature, moisture, food and so on. It is the number of offspring added to the population per female per week. At 29°C *Calandra* was able to multiply more rapidly than *Rhizopertha*, and it was *Calandra* that dominated the cultures, and *Rhizopertha* that became extinct. At 32°C the situation was reversed: *Rhizopertha* dominated and *Calandra* became extinct.

Table 11

Outcome when two grain beetles share the same resource

Species	*Temperature in °C*	*Finite rate of increase when alone*	*Survivor*	*Weeks for unsuccessful species to become extinct*	
				Mean	*Range*
Calandra	32	1·65	*Rhizopertha*	37	26 – 47
Rhizopertha	32	1·99			
Calandra	29	2·15	*Calandra*	—	38 – 190
Rhizopertha	29	1·75			

A number of experiments of this kind have now been done, and always with the same result. The species having the lesser capacity for increase is unable to maintain itself in the face of the growing population of the other species. Not all experiments have been as decisive as Birch's, however. For example, Park (1954) showed that when the capacities for increase of the two flour-beetles *Tribolium confusum* and *Tribolium castaneum* were only slightly different, the species with the lesser rate of increase became extinct in the culture tubes more often than not, although it was sometimes the species with the slightly greater capacity for increase that disappeared. This is what is to be expected, for the

•

capacity for increase of each species is measured in the absence of other species, and when the two are put together we could expect their capacities for increase to be slightly altered in the changed environment. Furthermore, the populations are usually started with a few adult beetles, and by chance the capacities for increase of some of these may differ from the average that had been estimated previously.

An unexpected yet consistent observation that is made whenever grain- or flour-beetles are cultured together in the laboratory is that the populations do not become dense enough to use up all their stocks of food. There is always some left when the time comes to replenish it, and yet one species always eventually dies out. The explanation of the results is complicated and not well understood, but space, and the habit beetles have of eating their own and other species' eggs and pupæ, have a bearing on the outcome of such experiments.

In other experiments the explanation is complete. For example, Black (1960) carried out a delightful experiment in which two

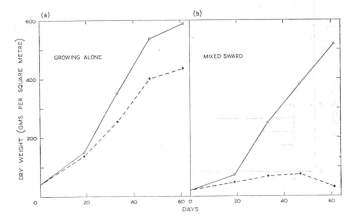

Figure 17

Changes in dry weight (a measure of growth) of the two strains of *Trifolium subterraneum* Yarloop (open circles) and Talarook (closed circles) (*a*) when each was grown alone, and (*b*) when the two strains grew together. After Black (1960).

strains of subterranean clover *Trifolium subterraneum* were sharing the same resource, namely, light. The strains of clover used, Yarloop and Talarook, are self-fertilising, and can be regarded here as if they were distinct species. Black planted each strain separately, and the two strains together in equal numbers, in seed-boxes at a density of 3000 plants per square metre. Nitrogen, water and all other resources except light were supplied in excess. At intervals he took samples of the sward, measured the dry weight of the plants (a measure of growth), the number and area of the leaves at different heights above the ground, and made measurements of the light intensity at different heights above the ground within the swards. Figure 17 shows the changes observed in the weight of the plants at intervals during the experiment, and it can be seen that although Yarloop grew larger than Talarook when each grew alone, when growing together Yarloop exceeded Talarook much more than might have been expected. This was partly due to the fact that in the mixed

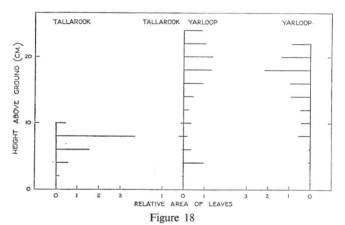

Figure 18

The horizontal lines represent the area of leaves at different heights above the ground, produced by the two strains of *Trifolium subterraneum*, Yarloop and Talarook. The side figures show the strains when grown separately. The central figure shows the areas of leaves produced by each strain when they were grown together, and illustrates the virtual suppression of Talarook through shading. After Black (1960).

sward 640 out of the 1500 plants of Talarook died, whereas no plants died in the pure stands. Yarloop grows taller than Talarook and when they grew together in this way Talarook did not get enough light to produce its full number of leaves, and many leaves died. Figure 18 illustrates this. The horizontal bars are a measure of the area of leaves at different heights above the ground, and it is clear that in the mixed sward Talarook was almost completely suppressed by the end of the experiment, because its leaves grew close to the ground and were thus shaded by the leaves of Yarloop. Table 12 shows the proportion of incident light absorbed by the leaves of each strain in the mixed stand. By day 47 no measurable light was penetrating to the leaves of the Talarook plants. The amount of light was limited, and because one strain was more efficient at utilising this resource and could therefore grow more rapidly than the other, it came to dominate the other strain completely.

Table 12

Percentage of incident light absorbed by Yarloop and Talarook growing together

	Day			
	19	33	47	61
Yarloop	75	99	100	100
Talarook	15	1	0	0

From these experiments we can conclude that when two species share the same limited resource, and when all other components of environment are kept constant, one of them is likely to persist and one to die out. But we cannot go one step further, with Lack (1954), and say that species with similar requirements cannot persist side by side in nature. Quite apart from the fact that two species with identical requirements would presumably be not two species but one, it is clear from Birch's work that if the temperature were fluctuating, as in nature, giving the advantages now to one species and now to the other, the most likely outcome would be the indefinite persistence of both species, with first one species in the ascendant and then the other. Some such state of affairs must be commonplace in nature, for we find many groups of species sharing the same resources and yet all are able to persist.

7.4

SOME OTHER WAYS IN WHICH ANOTHER
SPECIES MAY BE A COMPONENT OF ENVIRONMENT

We have now considered a number of ways in which an animal's chances of surviving and multiplying may be influenced by the numbers of other species that happen to be in its environment; we have considered how sheep aid and men restrict the distribution of ticks, how ladybirds kill and eat scale-insects, how pitcherplants kill and consume a variety of animals, and how grainbeetles use up the food or space, and clover plants the light, that other species also need. These are probably the most important ways in which different species enter each other's environment, but they are by no means the only ways. In this section a few other brief examples will be given.

The predators, mountain-lions and wolves, that preyed upon the deer on the Kaibab plateau were shot by men. The presence of man in the environment of the predators considerably reduced their chances of survival. But whereas killing a deer meant a meal and increased chances of survival and reproduction for the mountain-lion, the latter was not the case for man on killing a mountain-lion (unless having a lion-skin coat increased his chances of reproduction!). Similarly, dogs sometimes kill large numbers of sheep without eating them. This is a form of predation where there is no greater likelihood of an animal being killed by a predator as a result of some of its fellows having been preyed upon in the past. It may be unusual in nature, but it is common when man is the predator, particularly nowadays when wild animals are seldom killed for food; they are mostly killed with poison baits and sprays.

In South Australia the mosquito *Aedes alboannulatus* often lays its eggs in pools of water that collect in hoof-prints of cattle in mud. It sometimes happens that these are the only suitable places where *Aedes* can live. *Aedes* thus uses a resource provided by another species. Similarly, the water held in the pitchers of the pitcher-plant *Nepenthes* is used as a breeding place by nineteen species of animal, including one frog!

The French Bean *Phaseolus vulgaris* bears on its leaves epidermal hairs whose tips are bent over to form sharp hooks. Johnson (1953) showed that the hooks often impaled the legs of aphids

Aphis craccivora living on the beans, holding them fast. Usually a large aphid could release itself by pulling part of its leg off, but young aphids could not do this, and in struggling to free themselves often became caught in more than one place, were held down, were unable to feed and died. Johnson was unable to show that the bean made use of the aphids in any way. The upper surface of the bean leaf has few hooked hairs and Johnson was able to compare the fecundity and longevity of aphids living on the upper and lower surfaces of the leaves. On the upper surface a group of aphids lived, on the average, for more than fourteen days, and produced an average of three larvæ per day (these aphids are viviparous), whereas the group confined on the lower surface, among the hairs, lived on the average for only six days and produced rather less than half as many larvæ per day.

The traps set for rabbits by men can be regarded as essentially similar to the hooked hairs of *Phaseolus*. They are part of the animal's environment in that they reduce the animal's chance of survival, without necessarily increasing the chance of survival or reproduction of man who set them. The similarity between these two cases and the farmer weeding his land is clear.

The chance of survival of an animal or plant may be influenced by other species quite accidentally. Caterpillars living on a plant that is being eaten by sheep may get eaten along with the plant. And small ground-living animals and delicate herbs may be unable to survive the risk of being trampled upon by stock. In this way, sheep enter the environment of the caterpillar and the herb.

In section 7.1 we saw that the fences that limit the dispersal of *Ixodes* by confining sheep on a grazing were best thought of as an extension of man's activities. In the same way, the fence-post that is used by sheep to rub themselves, and that thereby sometimes crushes *Ixodes*, would not be there but for the farmer. So man is another species in the environment of *Ixodes* for a number of reasons. But when we enquire about the rocks that sheep use as rubbing-places we find that these are not due to the activities of any other animal but are part of the terrain that the animal happens to be living in. We shall discuss this, the fifth component of environment, in the next chapter.

8

Hazards

In Chapter 5 a 'resource' was defined as anything in an animal's environment that was used by the animal – for food, for building a nest, or in any other way. The criterion for a resource is that it is used by the animal whose ecology is being studied. Many resources are material things: sticks, stones or holes in the ground.

In Chapter 7 it was mentioned that when a man sets a trap that catches rabbits, or an ant-lion makes a pit that catches ants, we think of the trap or the pit in much the same way as we think of the claws of a cat that catches mice. Such material things, traps or pits, form a characteristic part of the predatory behaviour of man or the ant-lion, and are therefore best considered merely as characteristics of these particular predators, just as claws are characteristic of cats. The rabbit is part of man's environment, either as food or in some less direct way, and the ant is food for the ant-lion, and so is part of its environment. It will be shown in section 8.1 that it is only when the animal that is being studied is part of the environment of an animal that makes artefacts, like traps or pits, that the artefacts are best thought of as mere extensions of the other animal and so are best classified along with the members of other species.

But there are still some material things that enter into the environment of an animal – that is, that influence its chances of survival and reproduction – and yet that are not used by the animal in any way, and so are not resources; neither are they best thought of as extensions of another animal's activities. It will be convenient to call these things 'hazards'.

8.1

THE INFLUENCE OF HAZARDS
ON THE DISTRIBUTION AND NUMBERS OF ANIMALS

Fences and rocks on moorland grazings are used as rubbing-places by sheep. Ticks, especially females that have become swollen with blood, are likely to be squashed when the sheep rubs itself. Milne did not study this aspect of the tick's ecology in any detail, presumably because he felt it would contribute little to the causes of death among ticks, but nevertheless there is no doubt that these objects form part of the tick's environment. And it is likely that when there are many rubbing-places the chance of a tick being squashed is greater than when there are few.

Lampreys *Petromyzon marinus* were unknown in the great lakes of North America above Niagara Falls until the Welland canal was built. Then they were found attacking fish, at first in small numbers and later in sufficiently large numbers to reduce the catch of lake-trout *Salvelinus namaycush*. The falls thus acted as a barrier to the distribution of the lampreys and so influenced their chances of survival and multiplication (Elton, 1958).

In South Australia there are regions in which the red kangaroo *Macropus rufus* and the dingo *Canis dingo* live together, the dingo preying on the kangaroo. It is unusual to find kangaroos in large numbers in areas of large sand-hills and broad, smooth clay-pans, whereas they are frequently numerous in areas of stony desert soils. It is thought that the stones are too rough for the dingo but that the kangaroo is adapted to running rapidly on stony ground. The dingo's chance of catching a kangaroo is thus reduced on the stony country. The stones are thus part of the environment of both the dingo and the kangaroo; they reduce the dingo's chances of survival and reproduction, but they increase the kangaroo's chance, at least when dingos are present. How they influence kangaroos in the absence of dingos is not known.

Spring-tails, insects belonging to the Order Collembola, often become trapped and die in enormous numbers in the surface film on pools that collect in the hoof-marks left by bullocks in muddy ground. The collembolans are not killed by the bullocks, nor by any direct extension of the bullocks' activities, so it would not be appropriate to place the pools in the category 'members of other species', as we did with the ant-lion's pits and man's rabbit-traps.

Yet the distribution and numbers of pools undoubtedly influence the collembolans' chances of survival and multiplication. They are thus part of a collembolan's environment, and I shall call them hazards.

Artefacts, objects that are the result of the activities of man or other animals, often enter the environment of animals as hazards. For example, large spiders spin webs which may trap many minute insects and mites without in any way influencing the spiders' chances of survival and reproduction, and so without influencing the number of webs that will be spun. The producer of artefacts *par excellence* is man, and although many of his buildings, dams, drains and conveyances are used as resources by other animals, and his traps and bullets are best considered as part of his equipment as a predator, nevertheless, many of his artefacts influence animals' chances of survival and reproduction in ways which are not associated with his behaviour as a provider of resources or as a predator. They are best thought of as hazards for the animal. For example, cattle and sheep on large properties in Australia frequently become bogged and die in the mud on the edge of earthen dams. And populations of many animals have been reduced to low numbers, not by having been trapped or shot, but by having been restricted in the area over which they could disperse because of a fence or a canal. The sheep-tick is restricted in its distribution by fences built by man to confine sheep. In this case the fence is a hazard for the tick. It is strictly analogous to the waterfall that restricted the distribution of lampreys, with the exception that the waterfall was not the result of the activities of any animal.

Objects that are hazards for animals are most often not the result of the activities of any other species (unlike the pools in hoof-prints). But whether they are the result of the activities of another species or not, objects that are hazards all have this in common: their numbers and distribution are quite independent of the numbers of animals whose lives they influence. (They share this quality with certain resources – see section 5.13.) The hoof-marks mentioned in the last paragraph will be no more and no less numerous because few or many collembolans have drowned in them. This is because collembolans are *not* part of the bullocks' environment, they have no measurable influence on the bullocks' chances of surviving and reproducing. But bullocks are part of the collembolans' environment; they increase its hazards.

The environment of any animal can thus be analysed into five components: weather, resources, members of its own species, members of other species, and hazards. Each component of environment can influence the chances of survival and reproduction of the animal in a great diversity of ways, and it is part of the task of the student of populations to *describe* and *measure* the extent of the influence the environment has on the average individual in the population he is studying. He will then be able to use this information to help him explain the distribution and the numbers of the animals in the population.

The reason for classifying the environment in this way is to make it easier for an ecologist to think clearly about the relationship between an animal and its environment. It should also help him not to overlook some component in the environment of an animal he is studying, and to ensure that he will know the sorts of ways in which the various components of environment are likely to influence the numbers and distribution of the population. There may be times when he is uncertain into which category some component of environment falls. For example, it may be that other animals that aid in the dispersal of a species are best thought of as a resource – they can certainly be in short supply, in both an absolute and a relative sense (sections 5.12 and 5.13), and yet in Chapter 7 they were classified simply as members of other species. As we progress in our understanding, our classification is bound to change, probably radically. But precise classification is not really an important matter, so long as the measurements we make of the influence of each component of environment on the fecundity, length of life and speed of development of the animal we study are precise, and so long as we take full account of the influence the animal may exert on its environment. But it does seem that these conditions are most likely to be fulfilled when we have the clear understanding of the nature of environment that this classification seems to provide.

We have discussed a number of instances in which the influence of one component of environment was modified by other components. This is known as the interaction among components of environment. In the next chapter are described a few studies which illustrate the principle that components of environment seldom exert their influence on an animal independently of the other components.

Environment may sometimes influence survival in a direct way, as, for example, when an animal is caught by a predator, or becomes stuck in a bog, but often the influence is more indirect. As a result of a change in some component of environment, the *physiology* of an animal may be changed in a way which alters its fecundity, or longevity, or speed of development, and this may be reflected in changes in the numbers and distribution of the population. Or a changed environment may alter the animal's *behaviour* in some way, which may also be reflected in the population. The examples in the next chapter have been chosen to illustrate these ideas, too.

9

Behaviour and the
Interaction of Components of Environment

So far the discussion has been of ways in which individual components of environment may influence an animal's chances of survival and reproduction, and in the process nature has been made to seem simpler than it really is. The ecologist must learn to appreciate that the influence of one component of environment often depends on its interaction with some other component, or perhaps with several others; and the influence of the environment of the animal in its turn depends, often in a striking way, on the behaviour of the animal. The three examples to be discussed in this chapter have been chosen because they illustrate at least some of these complexities.

9.1

THE IMPORTANCE OF DISPERSAL
IN DETERMINING DISTRIBUTION AND NUMBERS

Melitaea harrasii is a small butterfly whose larvæ, at East Bluehill, Maine, feed exclusively on the leaves of *Aster umbellatus*. The butterflies lay batches of about 200 eggs unerringly on the leaves of *Aster* (a rather unusual accomplishment for butterflies – Dethier, 1959a). The young larvæ, which hatch in summer, are gregarious feeders until they reach the third instar. Then they disperse, pass the winter without feeding and complete their growth in spring as solitary feeders. The butterflies emerge in summer.

During his study of *Melitaea*, Dethier (1959b) did not find a single instance in which the larvæ that hatched from an egg-mass on an aster had enough food to complete their feeding without seeking another plant. Invariably, sooner or later, they consumed the entire plant and then had to disperse in search of another. By removing all the leaves from an aster except the one on which the larvæ were feeding, Dethier could force the larvæ to disperse when he wished, and he could count the numbers of larvæ that found new plants. The results depended largely on the distance to the nearest aster. In one experiment, 80% of newly-hatched larvæ died without finding a new source of food, although there were five asters within a radius of five feet. In another experiment 90% found food, but in this case about 40% found a plant only eight inches distant from the original plant. In other cases only about 20% managed to find a new source of food, although there was another aster within a radius of a few inches.

Dethier studied the movements of larvæ while they were on the ground. He found that they moved in a more or less straight line on cloudless days, or when the sun was exposed on cloudy days. The direction they took, that is, towards or away from the sun, seemed to be determined by the temperature of their bodies. When they were hot they moved away from the direction of the sun, and when they were cooler they moved towards the sun. But when clouds were passing over the sun at frequent intervals their course seemed to be quite disoriented. This is what might be expected, for Wellington (1955) has shown that caterpillars usually maintain their direction with respect to the plane of polarisation of light from the sky overhead. On a clear day this remains steady, but when clouds are passing over the sun the plane of polarisation of light changes rapidly, and so the direction of movement of the larvæ changes. Dethier concluded that the most important stimulus to which the larvæ were orienting was the sun, and the direction they took with respect to the sun was determined by the temperature of their bodies. But once having begun to move in a particular direction they maintained that direction with respect to the plane of polarisation of light from the sky overhead. When that changed, so their direction changed, giving the appearance, on cloudy days, of quite disoriented movement. He concluded, with Wellington, that overheating on sunny days was an important cause of death among wandering larvæ, and that most of their behaviour was directed towards preventing overheating. In sunny weather the larvæ would continue to walk in a particular direction, and in a dense population of asters would probably find one fairly quickly. But in cloudy weather, the changing plane of polarisation of light from the sky overhead so altered their behaviour that they had little chance of finding food.

By placing larvæ at different distances from asters, Dethier found that they were unable to perceive a new source of food except at a distance of a few millimetres. Furthermore, a young, gregarious larva that did manage to find an aster would not remain on it unless at least one other larva was also present. It would leave and wander again, often to perish. Dethier concludes that the large number of larvæ which succeed in finding food is principally due to the great density of aster plants.

East Bluehill is an area of woodland with open fields scattered sparsely through it. The fields are interconnected by roads. Asters grow only in the open, in fields and along roadsides, and although very little of the district is suitable for asters, they are nevertheless very abundant in the suitable spots.

A fortunate circumstance enabled Dethier to make a detailed study of *Melitaea* in relation to its food. The young gregarious larvæ spin a great deal of silk with which they bind the leaves of the aster against the stem. These leaves soon become brown, and the plants are easily recognised and can easily be counted. He estimated the average number of larvæ on each infested plant by counting all the larvæ on each of 50 plants and found that, on the average, each plant had 200 larvæ. Then, by choosing a period after all the eggs had hatched, and before any larvæ had begun to disperse, and counting all the asters on which larvæ were living, he was able to estimate the total number of larvæ in an area. In one field in which there were 9400 asters, he found that there were 14,200 larvæ on 71 plants at the beginning of the season. At the time of hibernation there were about 3000 larvæ left, and in the following spring 34 larvæ emerged from hibernation to feed. These gave rise to 19 butterflies! Dethier estimated that in the course of their development the larvæ from a single mass kill at most 5 plants. So the 14,200 larvæ would have eaten only 355 plants, or 3·8% of the available food. Yet about 80% of the larvæ died before hibernation. Some were killed by predators, but many from overheating and starvation while wandering from one food-plant to another.

Dethier also made a complete census of larvæ in an area of about seven square miles around East Bluehill. He found that there were a number of small, relatively isolated populations living in fields in the area; they would have been completely isolated were it not for the roadways along which butterflies move. But not all the fields or roadsides support a population of *Melitaea* – during 1958 there were only 21,200 larvæ in the area although there was enough food for many times this number.

The important point to be drawn from this study is that although the amount of food is great, and to a superficial observer apparently readily available, the larvæ experience a severe relative shortage of food, brought about by their innate behaviour. The shortage is still further aggravated by the influence of the weather on their behaviour. If the sky were always cloudless and the weather cool, we might expect that the larvæ would travel in fairly straight lines while dispersing and would thus perhaps find a greater proportion of the available food.[1] The behaviour of the females in laying large masses of eggs on single plants also aggravates the relative shortage of food for their larvæ because it ensures that they will be forced to move sooner or later from their original source of food to another, or starve. All these conditions tend to keep the population at a very low level relative to the stocks of food in the area. But Dethier found evidence that the numbers of *Melitaea* fluctuate widely over long periods of time. Extensive clearing and other practices tend to increase the *density* of the population of asters, so increasing the chances of survival of the dispersing larvæ, not merely because there is more food but because the plants are closer together and easier to find.

9.2

COMPLEX INTERACTIONS IN ENVIRONMENT

The muskrat *Ondatra zibethicus* lives in burrows close to water: either in the banks of streams or ditches, or beside lakes or swamps, or on islands in lakes or swamps. The opening of the

1. It may seem at first sight obvious that walking in a straight line would lead most quickly to a new source of food, because no time or energy would be wasted in searching places already searched, which is the case when the animal crosses its own tracks, as, say, in random movements. But on a spiral course the animal would not cross its own tracks, either. The problem of the most economical course to pursue has not been solved for this complex situation. The ecologist should beware of trusting the intuitively obvious.

burrow may often be under water. The food of the muskrat consists chiefly of plants in and around the water. Cat-tails *Typha latifolia* and bull-rushes are favourites, but many other species of plants, including crops, are eaten.

Muskrats are territorial animals, that is to say a pair of animals establish a burrow in which they live, and defend an area near the burrow from trespass by other muskrats. The breeding animals spend virtually their whole lives within the limits of their territory. In some places, such as permanent, lush swamps, where food and suitable places in which to make burrows are abundant, the territories tend to be small and the population of muskrats dense; in other places, such as along the banks of streams, the territories tend to be large and the population sparser. In an area where conditions are favourable, but where, for one reason or another, there are initially few muskrats, an increase in the population is accompanied by much fighting between the occupants of large territories and those trying to become established. The result is that the occupants of the territories are forced to give way, losing some of the outskirts of their territory, but hardly ever being ousted altogether. As the density of the population increases, and the territories become smaller and more easily defended, so it becomes less and less likely that a homeless muskrat will be able to force its way in, and if it survives the fighting it is compelled to live in a less favourable area. At such times there may be relatively large numbers of muskrats wandering about with no 'home' of their own.

The breeding season extends from spring through most of summer. The young produced in the first litter are tolerated in the territory until about the time of the birth of the next litter, when they are normally driven out and must establish territories for themselves. Similarly, the last-born young of the year are tolerated until breeding begins in the following spring, when they, too, are driven out to fend for themselves.

Drought, which leaves their burrows exposed and kills their food supply, and flooding, which fills their burrows with water and leaves them homeless, are considerable dangers to muskrats. Freezing of the soil in winter may force the muskrats from their burrows. A haemorrhagic disease caused by a micro-organism is common and sometimes kills large numbers of muskrats of all ages. The mink *Mustela vison* preys constantly on them.

Errington (1951) has studied the muskrat in the streams and swamps of Iowa for almost 30 years and has shown that the influence of the environment on the muskrat's chances of survival and reproduction can be quite involved because of the complexity of the interactions that occur between components of environment.

Errington says that when the level of water in a swamp is normal, muskrats can withstand a certain amount of trampling of their burrows by cattle and rooting by pigs without any measurable decrease in their numbers; they just dig a new burrow within their territory. But he adds: 'Nevertheless, disturbances of muskrats while handicapped by drought may not be within the capabilities of these animals to withstand, and wholesale mortality may be witnessed if conditions become sufficiently unfavourable.' Similarly, a drought that forces muskrats to wander far in search of food, or a flood that fills their burrows and forces them out on to higher ground, leaves them open to attack by mink.

In a sparse population living in a favourable area a young muskrat, forced out of the parental territory with the onset of the breeding season, may find a new territory close by without having to wander or fight the occupants of other territories. Under these circumstances the young are relatively safe from mink. But in a dense population the young, when they are evicted, engage in ceaseless strife with the occupants of the territories, trying to force their way in. They are usually unsuccessful and many of them are killed or maimed in the attempt. During this period they have no burrows to go to, and so must live in the open where they are likely to be found and eaten by mink. The lucky ones may find territories, less suitable than the ones from which they have been driven, and so extend the distribution of the population. But they are less likely to survive a drought or a flood, should it occur, because their territories are in 'marginal' areas and not so secure.

A population of muskrats that has become very dense is specially susceptible to disease, which may kill a high proportion of the animals, but this is less likely to occur in a sparse population. Sick muskrats often wander from their territories, and are then fiercely attacked by the occupants of neighbouring territories and may be attacked and killed by mink. But they are extremely likely to die in any case. Errington thinks that mink are unlikely to prey successfully on muskrats when they are living in their territories; it is only the wandering and sick muskrats that provide meals for mink. He further concludes that predators have little influence on the numbers of muskrats because most of the animals they take are almost certain to die from other causes in any case.

From this brief description it is clear that the influence of other animals and of resources on the chances of survival and reproduction of *Ondatra* depends very largely on the weather, and that the influence of mink depends on the numbers of other muskrats in the vicinity, on the weather and on disease (a member of another species). An interaction of four components of environment like this could be very complex indeed in its influence on the numbers of muskrats in a population.

9.3

INTERACTION BETWEEN RESOURCES

During the long, hot summer in the arid parts of Australia the red kangaroo *Macropus rufus* spends much of the day 'camping' in the shade of a bush or a tree. The red kangaroo is a large animal and it kicks out a shallow, dusty wallow in which to camp. In a specially favourable place, for example, under a spreading shrub that throws a dense shade, and about which one or two large bushes grow that may act as a wind-break, the wallow may be eight or ten feet long and perhaps three or four feet wide and may extend round the western, southern and eastern sides of the shrub, that is, round the whole of the part that is shaded at some time during the day. In a less favourable place, such as a bush that throws a patchy shade, the wallow may be only two feet long and one foot wide in the shape of a half-moon on the shady (southern) side of the bush. Near smaller bushes or tall trees with open canopies, it is unusual to find wallows; if kangaroos use these places at all, they do so in a much more transient way. But the favourableness of a particular bush or tree depends very much on the number of other bushes and trees in the neighbourhood. In country where there are many trees and a fairly dense underbrush, many apparently favourable places will have only a small wallow, indicating intermittent use by kangaroos, or no wallow at all, whereas on open plains where the vegetation consists chiefly of low shrubs, a single dense bush no more than three or four feet high usually has a large wallow extending over the whole area covered by the shade during the course of a summer's day. In wooded country there are so many good camping places that any one of them has a rather small chance of being used, whereas on plains where camping-places are few and far between, they are all likely to be used constantly.

In the dust of the kangaroos' wallows lives the kangaroo-tick *Ornithodoros gurneyi*, which feeds on the blood of kangaroos while they are lying in the shade. Unlike *Ixodes* (Chapter 1), *Ornithodoros* takes a full meal in an hour or so, and usually drops from its host to the ground in the same place from which it came. If the kangaroo should move off while the tick is feeding, the tick, when it falls to the ground, will burrow into the sand wherever it may be, but its chance of obtaining another meal if it is not in a wallow must be extremely small.

In South Australia kangaroos are fairly abundant in most of the dry pastoral country devoted to sheep-grazing. Figure 19 shows the limits of this area, bounded on the north by a high wire-mesh fence that effectively keeps the sheep country free from dingos, and on the south by the agricultural area from which kangaroos are excluded by the diligence of the farmers. The vegetation of most of this area consists of low bushes on which stock and kangaroos feed, a few widely scattered, tall trees, and intermittent dense shrubs which provide excellent camping-places for kangaroos. *Ornithodoros* is widely distributed as a sparse population throughout this kind of country. But there are some areas, particularly in the western and southern regions, where trees and large bushes are abundant, and although red kangaroos are also abundant *Ornithodoros* does not occur. Its absence from these areas is thought to be due to an interaction between the resources of the tick and the kangaroo. Where camping-places for kangaroos are in short supply, kangaroos are likely to use all of them regularly, so a tick living in one of them has a high probability of obtaining a meal. But when the supply of camping-places increases, any one of them is likely to be used rather seldom, and so a tick living in one would have only a small chance of obtaining a meal. The chance of a meal may be so small that the population cannot maintain itself. Of course, the probability of a camp being used depends not only on the density

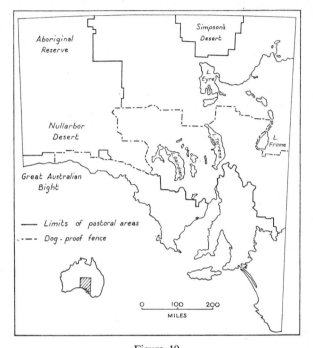

Figure 19

Map of South Australia, showing the limits of the arid sheep-grazing country.

of camps but also on the density of kangaroos, but the density of populations of kangaroos met with in South Australia seems never to be great enough to permit *Ornithodoros* to penetrate into well timbered country. And yet there is good reason to believe that ticks are constantly being carried into this kind of country, for the young tick taking its first meal differs from all the other stages in the tick's life-cycle in that it requires two to four days to complete its feed. It remains on the kangaroo during this time and so must often be carried quite long distances. This is probably the only stage in a tick's life when it can move from one wallow to another. And although ticks may be found living quite close to the margins of timbered country, and must frequently be carried in among the trees, they do not persist.

Both the kangaroo and the tick use the wallow as a shelter, but the tick uses the kangaroo as a source of food. An increase in the amount of shelter for kangaroos has little influence on the numbers of kangaroos; other components of the kangaroo's environment are more important in this respect. For this reason an increase in the amount of shelter for both kangaroos and ticks results in a decrease in the chances of survival and reproduction for the tick, because its other important resource, food, has become more difficult to find.

10

Self-regulatory Mechanisms

When ecologists speak of self-regulatory mechanisms in animal populations they are making an analogy with the governor of an engine, which speeds the engine up when it is slowing down and slows it down when it is speeding up, so tending to keep the fluctuations in the speed of the engine within rather narrow limits. They are referring to any situation in nature in which the chances of survival and reproduction of an individual in the population depend primarily on the numbers of other animals of its own kind in the vicinity, in such a way that the chances become less as the numbers increase, and *vice versa*. The examples that are the subject of this chapter are included here rather than in Chapter 6 because the phenomenon is not as yet well understood (though it is at present receiving considerable attention from ecologists), and deserves separate treatment. A number of examples of self-regulatory mechanisms have, in fact, already been given (*Tribolium* in section 6.11, voles in section 6.12, and muskrats in section 9.2). In this chapter the subject will be fitted into the general concept of animal ecology outlined in this book, as an extreme example of the influence of the numbers of an animal's own species on its fecundity, longevity and speed of development.

10.1

THE AUSTRALIAN MAGPIE

The magpie *Gymnorhina tibicen* is a bird of about the size and build of the European jackdaw, and it is one of the commonest birds in Australia. Carrick (1959) made a detailed study of these birds in an area of open savannah woodland and treeless downs near Canberra. He put distinctive leg-bands on a large number of birds that he caught alive, so that individuals could easily be recognised after they had been released. This enabled him to perceive two distinct elements in the population. Some birds lived among the trees in groups or 'tribes', each tribe consisting of between 2 and 8 birds: one pair of adults at least, with sometimes an additional male, females and juvenile birds. The members of a tribe remained within a well defined *territory* and fought together to defend it against encroachment by other magpies. Each territory contained at least one tree that was used as a nesting-place, and there was usually enough food and other resources within the confines of the territory for all the birds' needs. Young, sexually immature magpies usually remained in the territory for one or two years, but were then forced to leave as more young ones came on.

Other magpies lived in the treeless country in loose ' flocks ' which might consist of several hundred birds. These birds did not recognise territories, but some flocks remained within one relatively small area for long periods, while others moved about over distances of a few miles. The birds in the flocks were tolerant of other magpies in their vicinity, and when young magpies were driven from the parental territory they joined the flocks.

In the flocks Carrick often recognised a group, acting as a team, constantly trying to force its way into the area occupied by the territorial birds. Success was rare unless some calamity befell one of the tribes. If the male in a tribe died, the whole tribe was usually evicted from its territory, either by birds from neighbouring territories or by a group from the flock. If one of the females in a tribe died, her place was often taken by one or more females from the flock.

The birds in the flock did not breed. Even those that had bred while living in a territory ceased breeding if they were evicted. But most of the birds in the tribes bred each year. Usually they managed to hatch a high proportion of their eggs, but Carrick observed one tribe living in a minute territory that did not contain sufficient feeding-ground, in which the birds built the foundation of a nest but did not lay eggs. In another small territory the birds laid eggs, but the eggs became addled because of neglect – the female spent most of her time assisting the male to defend their boundary.

The death-rate among birds in the flock was often extremely high, mainly owing to disease, aggravated by the cold, wet winters. But the flocks persisted because their numbers were being continually added to by young birds that had been evicted as the territories became crowded, and by an occasional tribe that had lost its male.

The result of this complex behaviour was that the numbers of birds in the breeding population remained remarkably constant from year to year. Almost all the fluctuations in numbers occurred among the birds in the flocks. Within the territories the birds were secure even from disease, which decimated the birds outside. Furthermore, when females in the tribes died, the numbers in the tribes were made good by recruiting new females from the flock. And there were always groups of birds in the flock ready to harry and drive out a tribe that had lost its dominant male. In this way the number of tribes remained fairly steady even though the occupants of a territory changed.

The situation ensured that the magpies could maintain a high rate of reproduction from year to year in the best country, and yet there was no danger that they would use up a high proportion of their resources, or experience any of the dangers that are due to overcrowding.

There are a number of questions posed by this study that have not yet been answered, and that will well repay further study. Most birds become sexually active, that is, their gonads develop and produce mature eggs or sperm, in response to the changing seasons, probably mainly as a result of the changing length of day. But in the magpie this does not occur unless the bird is a member of a tribe living in a territory. In what way does the possession of a territory influence the hormones of the birds to enable them to become sexually active, when the birds without territories do not? There seems to be a close link between the psychology of the birds and the physiology of their hormone systems, which at the moment is not understood.

10.2

THE WESTERN TENT-CATERPILLAR ON VANCOUVER ISLAND

The moth *Malacosoma pluviale* lays its eggs in batches of about 100 to 300 eggs, attached to twigs of the plants on which the larvæ feed. The larvæ, when they hatch, spend a day or two congregated on top of the empty egg shells or moving about on the twigs and leaves. Then they begin to construct a communal silken 'tent', in which they shelter and moult. They emerge from the tent to feed, leaving a silken trail behind them as they go. They are strongly gregarious and tend to walk in procession when they move from one feeding-site to another.

Wellington (1957) found that he could distinguish three types of larvæ in *Malacosoma*. First, there were some that were very active, and that tended to walk rapidly in straight lines, laying a trail of silk as they went. If placed in a beam of light they would walk towards the light, and if placed on a twig on which there were leaves, they found the food quickly and began to feed. Secondly, there were some larvæ that were quite active, yet that, when placed in a beam of light, did not move consistently towards the light but turned continually this way and that, never making headway. If placed on a twig, a single larva of this kind never succeeded in finding the leaves. In a group these larvæ tended to congregate closely together, but they remained active and would follow each other's silken threads. Such a group did occasionally find food 'by accident', provided the food was close by. If one of the first kind of larva was placed in such a group, the group quickly followed the trail left by the active larva. Finally, there were larvæ that were extremely sluggish. A group of this kind would huddle together and remain almost motionless, but occasionally they would follow a thread left by a more active larva. They were never able to find food unless placed directly on it. Even then, if one fell off, it would starve although the food was only one centimetre away.

The most active larvæ ate more, and grew more quickly, than the intermediate kind, and the sluggish larvæ ate least and grew most slowly. Also, the most active larvæ tended to move away from their food to rest, leaving little silk on the food to entangle their droppings. A leaf on which these larvæ had been feeding was usually clean. The sluggish larvæ, on the other hand, remained on their food to rest, rested for longer periods between feeds, and covered their food with silk in which their droppings were caught. This almost always led to a disease that killed many of them by the time they reached their fifth instar.

Adults reared from the three kinds of larvæ showed similar differences. Active larvæ grew mainly into adults that flew readily, whilst sluggish larvæ developed into adults that tended to remain quiet and did not fly readily. The eggs laid by active moths gave rise to a high proportion of active larvæ, whereas from those laid by sluggish moths the proportion of active larvæ was much smaller.

Wellington took groups of larvæ of different types, put them in trees, thus forming artificial colonies, and observed their behaviour. One colony of 80 active larvæ constructed seven tents in four days, and fed on ten widely separated leaves. A comparable group of sluggish larvæ constructed one tent, fed on the leaf until it withered and then moved to another source of food 50 cm. away and constructed another tent. But in this case, when the group moved, many of the most sluggish larvæ were left behind in the first tent and starved. A group of the intermediate kind of larvæ was not very different in its behaviour from a sluggish group. But mixed colonies behaved very differently. When 20% of the larvæ were of the active kind and the remainder of the intermediate kind, the whole colony ranged almost as widely as a colony composed entirely of active larvæ; the intermediate kind followed the trails left by the active ones. But if some sluggish larvæ were included in the group, they were often left behind in abandoned tents and starved. Colonies composed entirely of sluggish larvæ always died from disease before they had completed their growth, whereas this did not usually happen to colonies of active larvæ.

A study of an area in which *Malacosoma* had been abundant for several years brought to light certain consequences of these differences in the behaviour of individual larvæ. In an area that had been infested for several years, most of the colonies consisted of all three kinds of individuals, with a great preponderance of the intermediate and sluggish kinds. These colonies fed on leaves close by their tent and severely defoliated the tree, but many larvæ died from disease or were left behind to starve in the tent when the colony abandoned it. The adults that arose from these colonies were also sluggish, and laid most of their eggs near the place where the larvæ had fed. On the other hand, colonies in areas that had not been infested in the previous year consisted of a preponderance of the active and intermediate kinds of larvæ. They ranged widely from their tent to feed and constructed several tents in the course of their development, and few of the larvæ died of starvation or disease. The adults that emerged from these colonies were also mostly of the active kind and laid their eggs widely, some near the places where they had fed as larvæ and some much further afield.

Wellington concluded from his studies that changes in the populations of *Malacosoma* are to be explained chiefly by considering the differences in the behaviour of individuals. A colony that arises in a new area, from eggs laid by an active female that has flown far from the place where she emerged, usually consists mainly of active and intermediate types of larvæ. During the course of its growth a colony of this kind would not seriously deplete its own food reserves, because these larvæ forage widely. The adults arising from such a colony would be of both the active and sluggish types, but the eggs laid in the vicinity of the colony would come predominantly from the sluggish females. The active females would lay some of their eggs there, but they tend to disperse widely. Thus the colonies of larvæ in the second generation would contain a much higher proportion of sluggish and intermediate individuals than the original colony did. The adults from these colonies would be predominantly of the sluggish kind, and the eggs laid in the vicinity would produce colonies made up predominantly of sluggish larvæ. By this time, that is, in the third year, the number of colonies close together and the constant intermingling of the larvæ would enable outbreaks of disease to spread from one colony to another. Furthermore, many individuals in these sluggish colonies would starve as larvæ or die as pupæ. The numbers would thus be greatly reduced in the vicinity of the original infestation. But elsewhere new populations would be starting out in the same cycle of increase and decrease in numbers.

As a population of *Malacosoma* increases in numbers, the increase in the proportion of sluggish individuals has one perhaps unexpected influence on the average chance of survival among the larvæ. The predatory fly *Tachinomyia similis* is more attracted to groups of larvæ than to individuals, although it will attack individuals if it encounters them. When a population contains a high proportion of sluggish larvæ, huddling together, these are more likely to be attacked by *Tachinomyia* than are the more active larvæ. But they are likely to die in any case, from starvation or disease, and if they do, the larvæ of *Tachinomyia* feeding inside their bodies will die too. So when sluggish individuals predominate in a population, they have the effect of protecting the more active individuals from attack by *Tachinomyia* and also of suppressing the numbers of *Tachinomyia* that survive to the next generation.

There is no doubt that the average length of life, speed of development and fecundity in many species of animals is strongly influenced by the numbers and kinds of its fellows that an animal has about it. Self-regulatory mechanisms now appear to be common among the vertebrates, and a few examples are known among the invertebrates. In the final chapter it will be considered how the ecological ideas that have been developed in this book may be applied to man, and whether self-regulatory mechanisms may operate in human populations, too.

11

Man's Place in
Animal Ecology, and the Ecology of Man

The discussion in this book has been full of examples in which man either directly or indirectly occupied a place in the environment of other animals. We have seen man as a predator of musk oxen and mountain-lions, and as a provider of transport for sheep and resources for many animals that feed on his crops or stock or live in his buildings. He may reduce the resources available for many species when he ploughs land or fells forests, drains swamps or builds dams, or he may increase resources through intensive agriculture or architecture. And he may introduce hazards into the environments of animals when he erects television aerials. He may even alter the weather to which animals are exposed with his central heating and steam pipes, or when he runs effluent from his chemical plants into rivers. It should thus be quite clear that when the ecologist sets about studying a population of animals he must usually take man and his activities into account.

There is one particular man that no ecologist can afford to neglect – himself. For just as in modern physics it is realised that the mere making of an observation may influence the thing to be observed, so the ecologist must always remember that every time he takes a sample of animals from a population, or interferes with it in any other way, he has to some degree changed the population or the environment of the animals. This is often of little moment and can usually be neglected, but sometimes, especially in small populations, it may be of considerable importance.

Thus it is appropriate to think of man as a member of another species when we study the ecology of an animal population. But man may also be regarded as an animal having the same five components in his environment as any other sort of animal. The rest of this book will attempt to suggest how this idea might help to explain the changes that occur in populations of men.

We have fairly accurate estimates of the numbers of men living on Earth, and of the way in which the numbers have changed in historical time. Figure 20 shows one such estimate. It is clear that the numbers of men have been increasing, with only minor checks, for at least 2000 years, and that the rate of increase has itself been increasing. This poses an ecological problem of some importance. How long is the human population likely to continue increasing, and what are the likely consequences of continued increase? One might also ask, although this is a problem in applied biology rather than in theoretical ecology, what steps could be taken to reduce the rate of increase or to stabilise or reduce the population?

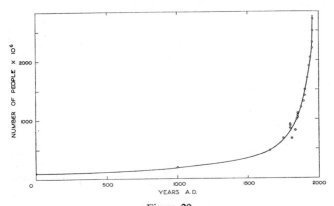

Figure 20

Trend in the numbers of men on earth. Data from von Foerster *et al.* (1960).

Civilised man has evolved to the point where he has become relatively independent of his environment. The weather does not often influence his chances of survival or reproduction, predators are of little consequence to him, even pathogenic bacteria and viruses are becoming of less consequence, and hazards he can usually avoid. The two components of environment that do seem to influence man's longevity and fecundity are his resources and the other members of his own species. If the difference between the birth-rate and the death-rate in the human population is to be reduced, it is likely to be because of the influence of one or both of these two components of environment.

The important resources on which man depends are food, minerals, fuel, fibres and fertilisers. Now all of these are already in short supply, at least locally. Furthermore, as more and more men come to understand that their own chances of surviving and leaving offspring can be enhanced by obtaining larger quantities of one or other of these resources, the shortage could become still more pronounced. To offset this trend, improved methods of technology in farming, in the extraction of low-grade ores, in the use of new fuels like uranium or deuterium, in the production of synthetic fibres, and in the extraction of phosphate from rocks, are all likely to provide much greater quantities of these resources. The supply may thus perhaps improve rather than worsen. But the absolute shortage of many resources is aggravated by a relative shortage brought about by the difficulties of exchange in modern commerce, leaving some parts of the population unable to obtain their requirements of some particular resource, even though in other places it is in super-abundance. One might anticipate, however, that with ingenuity and wisdom most of the problems of providing sufficient resources for a rapidly expanding population could be overcome, for a few generations at least. However, if the population continues to expand, sooner or later some resource or other will be depleted and result in a fall in the rate of increase, or in an actual decrease in the numbers of men.

It is worthwhile pursuing this idea a little further. Water is one of man's chief resources and it reacts to use in an unusual manner. The amount of new water available in the form of rain seems not to be influenced at all by the amount that is currently being used. It is likely that water will remain abundant and some other resource will give out sooner.

Of the resources likely to become scarce, minerals are of perhaps the most immediate concern. Man's use of minerals usually renders them unavailable to the next generation, or available only with great difficulty. He is thus depleting a pre-determined stock of minerals, at an increasing rate, and making the task of acquiring minerals more difficult for the next generation. The resources of other animals do not often react to use in this way.

Again, although food may be produced in increasing quantities to meet the demand of an expanding human population, the fertility of the soil is likely to be seriously depleted. Seriously impoverished and eroded soils, brought about by over-production, already deplete much formerly arable land. On the Kaibab plateau a similar state of affairs occurred when the numbers of mule-deer became great relative to their stocks of food (section 5.12), but at the rate the human population is increasing the result, if it occurs, will be much more spectacular.

The other component of environment that must be taken into account is other members of the species. It would seem that there are at least two ways in which this component of man's environment may bring about changes in the density of the human population. The first, and perhaps the most likely, is that one part of the population will attempt to reduce the density of another part by making use of the super-artefact – the hydrogen bomb. If this should occur it is possible that the whole problem of the human population will be solved once and for all.

Another way in which the rate of increase of the human population may be reduced is through some sort of self-regulatory mechanism (cf. Chapter 10). A study of the birth-rate in the densely crowded parts of the globe lends no support to the idea that increasing numbers will themselves cause a reduction in the birth-rate, for in many of the most crowded places the birth-rate is high. We get the strong impression that man is highly tolerant of crowding by his own kind. But there seem to be signs that things may not be quite so straightforward as they seem. In many crowded societies resources are in short supply and disease is common and often fatal. But there are other societies, in the great cities of Europe and North America, in which resources are, if anything, in super-abundance, and in which diseases due to pathogenic bacteria and viruses do not often cause early death. And it is in these societies, particularly, perhaps, among the people within these societies who have access to the greatest quantity and diversity of resources, that a number of diseases have become relatively much more common in recent years. Heart disease, neuroses of various kinds and serious ulceration of the digestive tract are mainly diseases of large cities and affluent societies. If it should turn out that, as the human population increases, the increase is more than offset by increased production of food and other resources, then it is just possible that men will react to crowding in a way similar to the voles at Lake Vyrnwy (section 6.12), by a great increase in the incidence of heart disease, neuroses and ulcers. All these things would increase the death-rate and reduce the birth-rate, and the population might then begin to decline, and continue to do so until the numbers reached a level at which these diseases no longer manifested themselves. Perhaps the human population is heading towards a series of oscillations in numbers brought about by the increased frequency of contact between individuals characteristic of crowding, and consequent increased incidence of certain diseases.

The ecology of human populations is much more complex than that of other animals, and this complexity is very largely due to man's imagination, which has led him to build up systems of mores, laws and customs that effectively isolate some sections of the population from others, and that lead to an unusual distribution of resources between members of the same local population. Just as among voles (section 6.12) and magpies (section 10.1) it was necessary to take the behaviour of the animals into account when trying to explain the numbers and distribution of the population, so it is necessary to take human behaviour into account when trying to explain the numbers and distribution of men. The study of sociology has for its subject-matter the social behaviour of human populations, and the study of demography is concerned with the numbers and distribution of men. Unfortunately, these two studies are all too often pursued quite independently of each other. If we are to reach a proper understanding of the ecology of man, someone will have to weld together sociology and demography, and show how each of these is illuminated by studies in human physiology and medicine.

References

I

Works taking a different view of animal populations from that taken in this book:

Allee, W. C., Emerson, A. E., Park, O., Park T., Schmidt, K. P. (1949), *The Principles of Animal Ecology*, Saunders, Philadelphia.
Clarke, G. L. (1954), *Elements of Ecology*, Wiley, New York.
Elton, C. S. (1927), *Animal Ecology*, Sidgwick and Jackson, London.
MacFadyen, A. (1957), *Animal Ecology: Aims and Methods*, Pitman, London.
Nicholson, A. J. (1954), An outline of the dynamics of animal populations, *Aust. J. Zool.* **2**, 9–65.
Odum, E. P. (1953), *Fundamentals of Ecology*, Saunders, Philadelphia.

II

The numbers appearing after each reference refer to the page on which the work is cited in the text. The list thus serves also as an index of authors. Key references to the ecology of the sheep-tick are marked with an asterisk.

Page

Andrewartha, H. G. and Birch, L. C. (1954), *The Distribution and Abundance of Animals*, Univ. of Chicago Press, Chicago   9

Andrewartha, H. G. and Browning, T. O. (1961), An analysis of the idea of 'resources' in animal ecology, *J. Theoret. Biol.* **1**, 83–97   9

Barton-Browne, L. (1956), The effect of light on the fecundity of the Queensland fruit-fly, *Strumeta tryoni* (Frog.), *Aust. J. Zool.* **4**, 125–145   56

Birch, L. C. (1945), The mortality of the immature stages of *Calandra oryzae* L. (Small Strain) and *Rhizopertha dominica* Fab. in wheat of different moisture contents, *Aust. J. exp. Biol. med. Sci.* **23**, 141–145   54

Page

Birch, L. C. (1953), Experimental background to the study of the distribution and abundance of insects, III, *Evolution* **57**, 136–144 — 83

Birch, L. C., Park, T. and Frank, M. B. (1951), The effect of intraspecies and interspecies competition on the fecundity of two species of flour beetles, *Evolution* **5**, 116–132 — 68

Black, J. M. (1960), The significance of petiole length, leaf area, and light interception in competition between strains of subterranean clover (*Trifolium subterranium* L.) grown in swards, *Aust. J. Agr. Res.* **11**, 277–291 — 85

Brett, J. R. (1952), Temperature tolerance in young Pacific salmon, Genus *Onchorynchus*, *J. Fish. Res. Bd. Can.* **9**, 265–323 — 45

Browning, T. O. (1952), The influence of temperature on the rate of development of insects, with special reference to the eggs of *Gryllulus commodus* Walker, *Aust. J. Sci. Res.* B **5**, 96–111 — 47

Browning, T. O. (1954), Observations on the ecology of the Australian field cricket, *Gryllulus commodus* Walker, in the field, *Aust. J. Zool.* **2**, 205–222 — 66

Browning, T. O. (1962), The environments of animals and plants, *J. Theoret. Biol.* **2**, 63–68 — 9

Carrick, R. (1959), The contribution of banding to Australian bird ecology (In Bodenheimer, F. S. and Weisback, W. W., *Monographie Biologicae* Vol. 8 Junk, The Hague) — 105

Chitty, D. (1952), Mortality among voles (*Microtus agrestis*) at Lake Vyrnwy, Montgomeryshire in 1936–9, *Phil. Trans. Roy. Soc. Lond.* B **236**, 505–552 — 71

Chitty, D. (1957), Self-regulation of numbers through changes in viability, *Cold Spr. Harb. Symp. Quant. Biol.* **22**, 277–280 — 71

Clarke, J. R. (1953), The effect of fighting on the adrenals, thymus and spleen of the vole (*Microtus agrestis*), *J. Endocrin.* **9**, 114–126 — 71

Dawson, J. (1956), Splenic hypertrophy in voles, *Nature* **178**, 1183–1184 — 71

Dethier, V. G. (1959a), Egg laying habits of Lepidoptera in relation to available food, *Canad. Ent.* **91**, 554–561 — 95

Dethier, V. G. (1959b), Food-plant distribution and density and larval dispersal as factors affecting insect populations, *Canad. Ent.* **91**, 581–596 — 95

Dice, L. R. (1952), *Natural Communities*, University of Michigan Press, Ann Arbor — 48

Page

Edney, E. B. (1953), The temperature of woodlice in the sun, *J. exp. Biol.* **30**, 331–349   49

Edney, E. B. (1957), *The Water Relations of Terrestrial Arthropods*, Cambridge Monograph in Experimental Biology, C.U.P., Cambridge   44

Elton, C. S. (1927), *Animal Ecology*, Sidgwick and Jackson, London   61

Elton, C. S. (1958), *The Ecology of Invasions by Animals and Plants*, Methuen, London   73, 91

Errington, P. L. (1951), Concerning fluctuations in populations of the prolific and widely distributed muskrat, *Amer. Naturalist* **85**, 273–292   100

Finney, D. J. (1947), *Probit Analysis*, C.U.P., Cambridge   46

Von Foerster, H., Mora, P. M. and Amiot, L. W. (1960), Doomsday: Friday 13 November, A.D. 2026, *Science* **132**, 1291–1295   113

Ghent, A. W. (1960), A study of the group-feeding behaviour of larvae of the jack-pine sawfly, *Neodiprion pratti banksianae* Roh., *Behaviour* **16**, 110–148   74

Hinton, H. E. (1951), A new chironomid from Africa, the larva of which can be dehydrated without injury, *Proc. Zool. Soc. Lond.* **121**, 371–380   54

Hone, E. (1934), The present status of the muskox, *Am. Comm. Int. Wildl. Prot. Spec. Pubn.* **5**, 1–87   73

Huntsman, A. G. and Hoar, W. S. (1939), Resistance of Atlantic salmon to sea water, *J. Fish. Res. Bd. Can.* **4**, 409–411   56

Johnson, B. (1953), The injurious effect of the hooked epidermal hairs of French beans (*Phaseolus vulgaris* L.) on *Aphis craccivora* Koch, *Bull. Ent. Res.* **44**, 779–788   88

Kennedy, J. S. and Booth, C. O. (1951), Host alternation in *Aphis fabae* Scop., *Anns. appl. Biol.* **38**, 25–64   65

Kluijver, H. N. (1951), The population ecology of the great tit *Parus m. major*, *Ardea* **39**, 1–135   61

Krogh, A. and Zeuthen, E. (1941), The mechanism of flight preparation in some insects, *J. exp. Biol.* **18**, 1–10   44

Lack, D. (1954), *The Natural Regulation of Animal Numbers*, Clarendon Press, Oxford   87

*Lees, A. D. (1946), Water balance in *Ixodes ricinus* L. and certain other species of ticks, *Parisitol.* **37**, 1–20   14, 50

*Lees, A. D. (1948), The sensory physiology of the sheep-tick *Ixodes ricinus* L., *J. exp. Biol.* **25**, 145–207   14

Page

*Lees, A. D. and Milne, A. (1951), The seasonal and diurnal activities of individual sheep-ticks (*Ixodes ricinus* L.), *Parisitol.* **41,** 189–208   14

Leopold, A. (1943), Deer irruptions, *Wis. conserv. Bull.* **8,** 4–11   59,80

Lloyd, F. L. (1942), *The Carnivorous Plants*, Chronica Botanica Co., Mass.   81

Lorenz, K. and Tinbergen, H. (1938), Taxis und Instinkthandlung in der Eirollbewegung der Graugans, *Zs. Tierpsychol.* **5,** 235–409   66

Madge, P. E. (1956), The ecology of *Oncopera fasciculata* (Walker) (Lepidoptera: Hepialidae) in South Australia III, *Aust. J. Zool.* **4,** 346–357   49

*Milne, A. (1950), The ecology of the sheep-tick *Ixodes ricinus* L. Spatial distribution, *Parisitol.* **40,** 35–45   12

Park, T. (1954), Experimental studies of interspecies competition II, *Physiol. Zool.* **27,** 177–238   84

Potts, W. H. and Jackson, C. H. N. (1952), The Shinyanga game destruction experiment, *Bull. ent. Res.* **43,** 365–374   64, 72

Rasmussen, D. I. (1941), Biotic communities of Kaibab plateau, Arizona, *Ecol. Monogr.* **11,** 230–275   59

Schmidt-Nielsen, B. and Schmidt-Nielsen, K. (1951), A complete account of the water metabolism in kangaroo rats and an experimental verification, *J. cell. comp. Physiol.* **38,** 165–182   51,53

Solomon, M. E. (1951), Control of humidity with potassium hydroxide, sulphuric acid, or other solutions, *Bull. ent. Res.* **42,** 543–554   49

Southwick, C. (1958), Population characteristics of house-mice living in English corn ricks: density relationships, *Proc. Zool. Soc. Lond.* **131,** 163–175   70

Thompson, R. C. M. (1951), *Mosquito Behaviour in Relation to Malaria Transmission and Control in the Tropics*, Edward Arnold, London   56

Utida, S. (1957), Population fluctuation, an experimental and theoretical approach, *Cold Spr. Harb. Symp. Quant. Biol.* **22,** 139–151   78

Vance, A. M. (1949), Some physiological relationships of the female European corn borer moth in controlled environments, *J. econ. Ent.* **42,** 474–484   48

Waterhouse, D. F. (1947), The relative importance of live sheep and of carrion as breeding grounds for the Australian sheep blowfly *Lucilia cuprina*, *Bull. Counc. Sci. Indust. Research*, Australia, No. 217   59

Page

Wellington, W. G. (1955), Solar heat and plane polarized light versus light compass reaction in the orientation of insects on the ground, *Ann. Ent. Soc. Amer.* **48,** 67–76   96

Wellington, W. G. (1957), Individual differences as a factor in population dynamics: the development of a problem, *Canad. J. Zool.* **35,** 293–323   108

Wheeler, W. M. (1930), *Demons of the Dust*, Kegan Paul, London   82

Index